CONT

PREFACE

Critics have said that we Americans have despoiled our land, wasted our natural resources, polluted our water and air, leveled our forests, and decimated our wild plants and animals. However, as a nation, we have made much progress in recognizing our mistakes and inadequacies and are taking steps to correct them. Among these steps, and related to this publication, are the Missouri Threatened and Endangered Species Act of 1972, the National Endangered Species Act of 1973, and the Renewable Resources Planning Act of 1974. At first these laws pertained primarily to animal species, but they have since been applied to plant species.

Interest in rare, unique, threatened, and endangered plant species has greatly intensified over the past five years. This interest will undoubtedly increase in the Ozark Plateau area as both the activities of the conservation and preservation organizations, and the funding of the Missouri Department of Conservation provided through the **Design for Conservation** Program increase. The current policy and management direction of the U.S. Forest Service's Mark Twain National Forest and the Columbia, Missouri Unit of the North Central Forest Experiment Station promise to complement these efforts and interests.

The variety, diversity, and uniqueness of the Ozark Plateau make its flora of special interest. The Ozark Plateau is one of the few areas of the North American mainland to escape both flooding and glaciation since its formation over 200 million years ago. Consequently, some of the plants represent a long progression in the evolutionary development of a species. Another remarkable fact is that the Ozarks are a focal point of several converging ecosystems: namely, the eastern hardwoods, the southern pine, and the western prairies. Some relic species are found here and then found again much farther north. It is believed that these species migrated southward during the Pleistocene glaciation and have persisted in special habitats as remnant populations.

HOW TO USE THIS GUIDE

Most small, popularized identification guides begin with the message that, "hopefully this guide will facilitate the identification of species most likely to be encountered." We present this booklet with a different message. We hope this guide will stimulate your interest in searching for, identifying, and reporting findings of those plant species that are **least** likely to be encountered on an average outing.

The joys of discovery and aesthetic appeal of plant species provide rewarding experiences for the observer. In addition, the study of plants is one field of the biological sciences where the contributions of amateurs are very important. Very little is known of the locations, status, and life requirements of many of these plants. Often a simple listing of species in an area where rare species might be found is a great contribution to knowledge of plant distributions.

The main purpose of this guide is to stimulate you—the amateur botanist—to look for these plants and provide notes on them and their associated species, and on the habitat in which they are found. Such information will help public land managers formulate plans to ensure the preservation of these rare plants.

The plants are grouped into five broad groups according to habitat: 1) woodlands; 2) glades, including bluffs and rocky slopes; 3) wet lowlands, including swamps, swales, bogs, and wet woods; 4) aquatic habitats, including sinkholes, streams, and ponds; and 5) prairies, including fields and meadows. Because these groupings are somewhat artificial, and because some plants are at home in several environments, you should check the possibility that a plant you have found is listed in a habitat group other than the one you first turn to. To help you make this check, at the end of each habitat grouping is a list of plants whose habitat requirements are broad enough that they are sometimes found in two or more of our habitat classifications.

Each plant description includes its national status, its status in Missouri, or both. We obtained the national status information from the **Endangered and Threatened Species—Plants,** prepared by the USDI Fish and Wildlife Service in 1976. The status in Missouri comes from the **Rare and Endangered Species of Missouri** prepared by the Missouri Department of Conservation and the USDA, Soil Conservation Service, in 1978.

The definitions of plant status are as follows:

National

Endangered: Those species of plants in danger of extinction throughout all or a significant portion of their ranges.

Threatened: Those species of plants that are likely to become endangered within the foreseeable future throughout all or a significant portion of their ranges.

Missouri

Endangered: A species whose prospects for survival within the state are in immediate jeopardy.

Rare: A species, although not presently threatened with extirpation, is in such small numbers that it could easily become endangered if its environment worsens.

Status Undetermined: A species that has been suggested by competent authority as possibly rare or endangered, but about which there is not enough information to determine its status.

Known locations of each plant are listed by counties. A Missouri county map is included at the end of this section for your convenience.

An illustrated glossary is included on page 225 at the back of the guide for the technical terms used in the plant descriptions.

We publish this identification guide with some reservations. We sincerely hope that you will recognize the perilous situation of many of these plants and strive, along with us, to provide them adequate protection. PLEASE DO NOT COLLECT or otherwise disturb these plants if you find them. Instead, please send the information requested in the Rare Plant Observation Data form found on page 237 at the end of the guide to:

> Natural History Officer
> Missouri Department of Conservation
> P.O. Box 180
> Jefferson City, MO 65101

MAP OF
MISSOURI COUNTIES

4

LIST OF SPECIES BY HABITAT AND FAMILY

FAMILY	SCIENTIFIC NAME	COMMON NAME	PAGE

GLADE (BLUFF AND ROCKY WOODED SLOPE) SPECIES

FAMILY	SCIENTIFIC NAME	COMMON NAME	PAGE
CUPRESSACEAE	Juniperus ashei	Ashe Juniper	74
GRAMINEAE	Calamagrostis insperata	Reed Bent Grass	76
GRAMINEAE	Sporobolus neglectus var. ozarkanus	Bald Grass	78
LILIACEAE	Zigadenus nuttallii Gray	Death Camas	80
LILIACEAE	Yucca glauca var. mollis	Soapweed	82
POLYGONACEAE	Eriogonum longifolium	Umbrella Plant	84
POLYGONACEAE	Polygonella americana	Jointweed	86
NYCTAGINACEAE	Mirabilis linearis	Four O'clock	88
CARYOPHYLLACEAE	Geocarpon minimum	Geocarpon	90
RANUNCULACEAE	Delphinium treleasei	Trelease's Larkspur	92
BERBERIDACEAE	Berberis canadensis	American Barberry	94
CRUCIFERAE	Lesquerella filiformis	Bladder-pod	96
SAXIFRAGACEAE	Heuchera missouriensis	Missouri Alumroot	98
SAXIFRAGACEAE	Ribes odoratum	Golden Currant	100
LEGUMINOSAE	Amorpha brachycarpa	Hairless Leadplant	102
EUPHORBIACEAE	Phyllanthus polygonoides	Spurge	104
MALVACEAE	Callirhoe papaver var. bushii	Poppy-mallow	106
HYPERICACEAE	Hypericum densiflorum	Bushy St. John's-wort	108
ONAGRACEAE	Stenosiphon linifolius	Flax-leaved Stenosiphon	110
GENTIANACEAE	Centaurium texense	Centaury	112
APOCYNACEAE	Amsonia ciliata var. filifolia	Ciliate Blue Star	114
ASCLEPIADACEAE	Asclepias meadii	Mead's Milkweed	116
POLEMONIACEAE	Phlox bifida var. stellaria	Sand Phlox	118
SCROPHULARIACEAE	Penstemon cobaea var. purpureus	Purple Beard-Tongue	120
RUBIACEAE	Galium boreale var. hyssopifolium	Northern Bedstraw	122
COMPOSITAE	Liatris mucronata	Blazing Star	124
COMPOSITAE	Erigeron pusillus	Daisy Fleabane	126

6

WOODLAND SPECIES

NIMBLE WILL

FAMILY:
 GRAMINEAE

SCIENTIFIC NAME:
 Muhlenbergia schreberi var. *curtisetosa* (Scribn.)
 Steyerm. and Kucera

STATUS:
 National list - threatened
 Missouri list - rare

POSSIBLE LOCATIONS:
 Barry County—Eagle Rock

HABITAT:
 Woodlands

DESCRIPTION:

Flowering time:
 July-November; perennial.

Flower:
 Panicles slender; glumes whitish, minute, **1.5
 mm long; lemma 3 mm long** with awn 3 mm in
 length.

Leaves:
 Sheaths compressed; leaf blades short,
 spreading to 3-4 mm wide.

Stem:
 Up to 50 cm high; slender, much
 branched,reclining; rooting at lower nodes;
 plant forms bunches.

Muhlenbergia schreberi var.curtisetosa

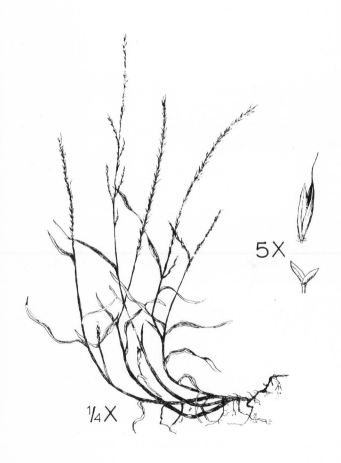

5X

¼X

OZARK WAKE ROBIN

FAMILY:
LILIACEAE

SCIENTIFIC NAME:
TRILLIUM PUSILLUM Michx. var. *ozarkanum*
(Palmer and Steyerm.) Steyerm.

STATUS:
National list-threatened;Missouri list-endangered

POSSIBLE LOCATIONS:
Barry County—3 miles south of Cassville along
   Highway 112 and along road to Roaring River
   State Park.
Lawrence County
McDonald County—near Rocky Comfort
Shannon County—west side of Highway 80,
   T.27N., R.5W., Sec. 34, 2 mi. south of Birch
   Tree
Taney County—woods north of the School of the
   Ozarks Dairy

HABITAT:
Dry, wooded slopes and acid soils

DESCRIPTION:
Flowering time:
   April-early May; perennial.
Flower:
   Vary in color from white to pink to **pink or
   rose-purple;** on a peduncle; petals 2-3 cm long,
   assume a flat-horizontal spreading position.
Leaves:
   2-8.5 cm long; in 1 whorl of 3 leaves **without a
   leafstalk;** membranaceous, soft in texture; dull
   grass green on both sides.
Stem:
   10-30 cm tall; slender.
Fruit:
   Peduncle remaining erect in fruit.

WOODLAND
Trillium pusillum var. ozarkanum

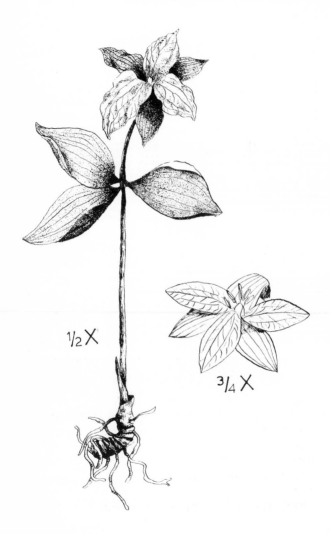

1/2 X

3/4 X

SPIDERWORT

FAMILY:

  COMMELINACEAE

SCIENTIFIC NAME:

  Tradescantia ozarkana Anderson and Woodson

STATUS:

  Missouri list - endangered

POSSIBLE LOCATIONS:

  Along the White River and its tributaries
  Barry County—Roaring River stream in "Brunner
    Hollow" on east facing slope
  Ozark County
  Stone County
  Taney County

HABITAT:

  Wooded slopes and ravines or roadsides

DESCRIPTION:

  Flowering time:

    April-June; perennial.

  Flower:

    Petals vary from white to pink; 3 petals are
    equal and alike; not surrounded by a folded
    spathe; **sepals 4-10 mm long, not inflated.**

  Leaves:

    Leaf blades 15-50 mm wide and hairless ex-
    cept for margins; succulent; silvery or gray-
    green and **slightly glaucous.**

  Stem:

    Small plants with short stems 2-10 cm tall and
    crowded leaves; or plants averaging 15-70 cm
    tall.

WOODLAND
Tradescantia ozarkana

1X

½ X

½ X

LOESEL'S TWAYBLADE

FAMILY:
ORCHIDACEAE

SCIENTIFIC NAME:
Liparis loeselii (L.) Richard

STATUS:
Missouri list - endangered (relic)

POSSIBLE LOCATIONS:
Shannon County—alder thicket valley of Big Creek, T.31N., R.2W., Sec. 5.

HABITAT:
Damp or wet woods, bogs, and damp thickets

DESCRIPTION:

Flowering time:
May-June; perennial.

Flower:
Yellow-green; loose raceme of 2-25 flowers, each flower on a short stem; petals somewhat reflexed, lip is **4-5 mm long** with upturned margins.

Leaves:
Only 2 located at base of plant, 5-15 cm long and 2-7 cm wide; yellow-green; strongly keeled; present at flowering time.

Stem:
0.5-3 dm high; swollen at base.

Roots:
Bulb.

WOODLAND
Liparis loeselii

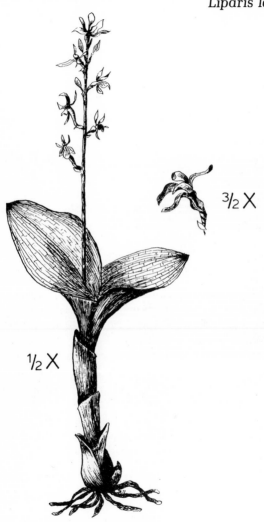

3/2 X

1/2 X

GREEN ADDER'S MOUTH

FAMILY:
ORCHIDACEAE

SCIENTIFIC NAME:
Malaxis unifolia Michx.

STATUS:
Missouri list - rare

POSSIBLE LOCATIONS:
Dent County
Green County
Howell County
Ste. Genevieve County
Shannon County

HABITAT:
Dry or damp woods, bogs

DESCRIPTION:

Flowering time:
May-June; perennial.

Flower:
Flowers minute; greenish; lip 2-2.5 mm long; petals threadlike, reflexed; lip 2 lobed with a small tooth in the sinus; 5-35 flowers in a raceme.

Leaves:
3-6 cm long; **1** (rarely 2); pale or grass green; **sessile, oval or elliptic; located about halfway up the flowering stem;** present at flowering time.

Stem:
0.5-3 dm high.

WOODLAND
Malaxis unifolia

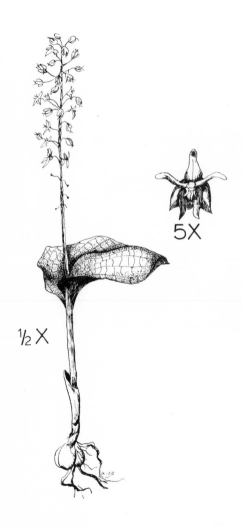

5X

½ X

RATTLESNAKE PLANTAIN

FAMILY:
ORCHIDACEAE

SCIENTIFIC NAME:
Goodyera pubescens (Willd.) R. Br.

STATUS:
Missouri list - rare

Edge of geographical range

POSSIBLE LOCATIONS:
Douglas County
Iron County
Reynolds County
St. Francois County—Hickory Canyons Natural
Area.
Ste. Genevieve County—Pickle Springs; 7 miles SE
of Farmington on Highway 32, 1½ miles west on
County Road AA.

HABITAT:
Well-drained, moist soils in narrow upland valleys

DESCRIPTION:

Flowering time:
July to mid-September; perennial.

Flower:
White or greenish; inflorescence dense; lip
subglobose with short blunt tip.

Leaves:
3-6 cm long; ovate or lance-ovate; **dark green
with 5-7 white veins and numerous white
reticulate veinlets** arranged in a rosette at the
plant base.

Stem:
2-4 dm high; stout

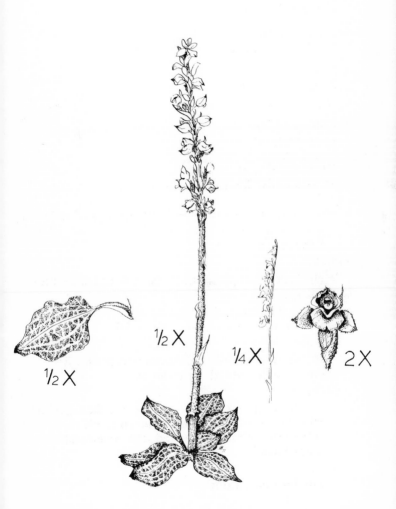

½ X

½ X

¼ X

2 X

LARGE WHORLED POGONIA

FAMILY:
ORCHIDACEAE

SCIENTIFIC NAME:
Isotria verticillata (Willd.) Raf.

STATUS:
Missouri list - rare
Edge of geographical range

POSSIBLE LOCATIONS:
Butler County—vicinity of Poplar Bluff
Ste. Genevieve County—along Pickle Creek, about
¼ mile down valley from Pickle Spring, T.36N.,
R.7E., about 6 miles SE of Sprott.

HABITAT:
Dry woodland

DESCRIPTION:

Flowering time:
May; perennial.

Flower:
Sepals 3.5-6 cm long, linear, colored dull brown-
purple above and yellow-green below; **petals
½-⅓ as long as the sepals;** lateral petals yellow-
green, lip green on the main portion with a
larger white lobe and a smaller white and purple-
striped lateral lobes.

Leaves:
3-8 cm long; **5-6 (rarely up to 10) arranged in a
circle at the top of the stem;** leaves present at
flowering time.

Stem:
2-4 dm high; slender.

Fruit:
2.5-3.5 cm long; fruit stalk 2.5-6 cm long.

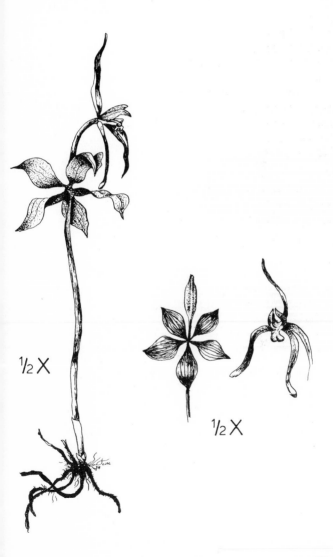

½ X

½ X

OZARK CHINQUAPIN

FAMILY:
FAGACEAE

SCIENTIFIC NAME:
Castanea ozarkensis Ashe

STATUS:
National list - endangered

POSSIBLE LOCATIONS:
Barry County

Stone County

McDonald County

Wayne County

Newton County

HABITAT:
Woods and rocky slopes

DESCRIPTION:

Flowering time:
Late May to June.

Flower:
Either male or female; male in long upright ament; female usually 3 together in a scale; prickly involucre; fragrant.

Leaves:
15-20 cm long; yellow or grass-green on upper surface; **minutely hairy on lower surface;** margins are coarsely toothed, teeth 3-8 mm long.

Stem:
Tree; up to 20 m high (65 ft).

Fruit:
Spines hairy and 1-1.3 cm long; **each fruit with only 1 nut, not flattened.**

Note: Nuts are sweet and edible. This tree is endangered because of chestnut blight. Any reported sightings should include whether or not the tree is infected.

WOODLAND
Castanea ozarkensis

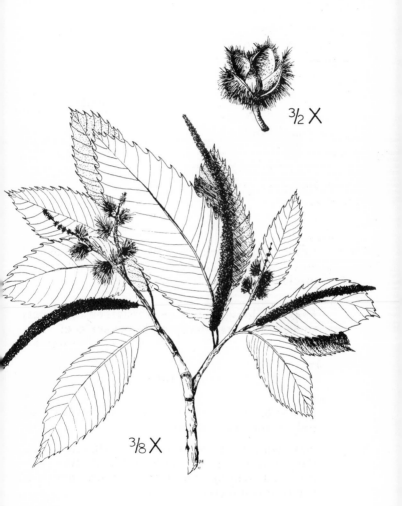

3/2 X

3/8 X

25

WEAK NETTLE

FAMILY:
URTICACEAE

SCIENTIFIC NAME:
Urtica chamaedryoides Pursh

STATUS:
Missouri list - undetermined

POSSIBLE LOCATIONS:
Barry County
McDonald County
Pemiscott County
Stone County
Taney County

HABITAT:
Bottomlands, moist woods, and thickets

DESCRIPTION:

Flowering time:
April-September; annual.

Flower:
Greenish, minute; in clusters of 1-2 in each axil; usually shorter than the leaf stalks.

Leaves:
1.5-7.5 cm long; **upper smaller than middle or lower;** margins coarsely toothed, **teeth blunt, the sides curved.**

Stem:
3-8 dm high; slender; branched from the base; has stinging hairs.

WOODLAND
Urtica chamaedryoides

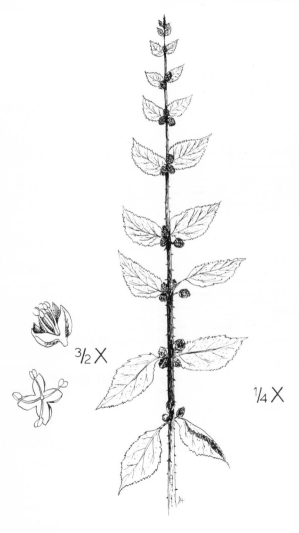

³⁄₂ X

¹⁄₄ X

27

FALSE BUGBANE

FAMILY:
RANUNCULACEAE

SCIENTIFIC NAME:
Trautvetteria caroliniensis (Walt.) Vail

STATUS:
Missouri list - rare (one of the rarest wildflowers in
Missouri)

POSSIBLE LOCATIONS:
Shannon County—along Jack's Fork and Current
Rivers.
—Moist limestone cliffs of Jack's Fork of Current
River near Montier.

HABITAT:
Banks of streams, wooded bluffs, and prairies

DESCRIPTION:

Flowering time:
June-August; perennial.

Flower:
No petals; 3-5 white sepals; **in cormybiform
clusters.**

Leaves:
1-4 dm broad; **3 or more on the stem;** basal
leaves are long-stalked, with 5-11 irregularly-
toothed lobes.

Stem:
5-15 dm tall.

Fruit:
Green to brown; dry.

WOODLAND
Trautvetteria caroliniensis

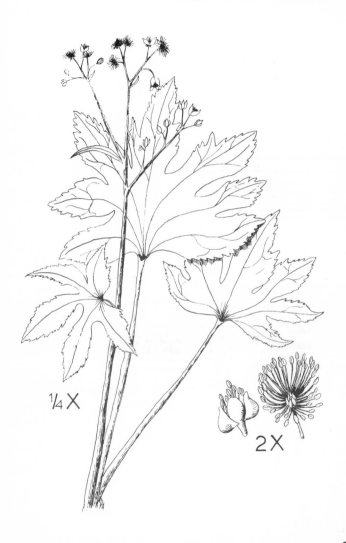

¼X

2X

TALL LARKSPUR

FAMILY:
RANUNCULACEAE

SCIENTIFIC NAME:
Delphinium exaltatum Ait.

STATUS:
Missouri list - rare

Edge of geographical area

POSSIBLE LOCATIONS:
Howell County—South Fork of Spring River.
Shannon County—Current River, Jack's Fork of
Current River and tributary streams.

HABITAT:
Rich woods, thickets, and rocky slopes

DESCRIPTION:

Flowering time:
July-August; perennial.

Flower:
1.4-2.2 cm long; purple, pale blue, or whitish
with lavender; with a spur; lower petal not split
into two; **pedicels 1-2.5 cm long.**

Leaves:
Large; pale beneath; deeply 3-5 cleft; **wedge-
shaped.**

Stem:
0.6-2 dm high; slender; **without hairs below the
inflorescence.**

Fruit:
Seeds have a loose cellular coat; **wrinkled, not
covered with scales.**

WOODLAND
Delphinium exaltatum

1X

½X

LEATHER FLOWER

FAMILY:
  RANUNCULACEAE

SCIENTIFIC NAME:
  Clematis viorna L.

STATUS:
  Missouri list - rare

POSSIBLE LOCATIONS:
  Bollinger County
  Taney County
  Wayne County

HABITAT:
  Moist woods and thickets, around limestone bluffs

DESCRIPTION:

Flowering time:
  May-July.

Flower:
  1.5-4.5 cm long, bell-shaped; formed by purplish, bluish, brown-lavender or lavender and
  green sepals that are **joined together for most of
  their length;** sepal tips recurving; **styles feathery
  with spreading hairs in the fruiting stage.**

Leaves:
  Bright green; entire 2-3 lobed on petioles; hairy
  on lower surface.

Stem:
  Climbing, sprawling, or trailing vine.

WOODLAND
Clematis viorna

½ X

¾ X

½ X

WHITLOW GRASS

FAMILY:
CRUCIFERAE

SCIENTIFIC NAME:
Draba aprica Beadle

STATUS:
National list - endangered
Missouri list - endangered
Edge of geographical range

POSSIBLE LOCATIONS:
Barry County
Madison County—St. Francis "Shut-ins," 14 miles
south of Fredericktown.
base of Tin Mountain near
Cedar Bottom Creek.

HABITAT:
Woods and clearings

DESCRIPTION:

Flowering time:
April-May; annual.

Flower:
Petals white when present; some flowers with
petals, some without.

Leaves:
0.7-2 cm long; scattered up and down length of
stem; lower leaves coarsely 2-4 toothed, thin,
petioled; cauline leaves narrow, entire.

Stem:
0.5-3.5 dm high; **usually unbranched,** slender;
**usually with small short corymbs in the middle
and upper axils.**

Fruit:
Minutely hairy.

WOODLAND
Draba aprica

7/2 X

5/2 X

1/2 X

35

EASTERN WITCH HAZEL

FAMILY:
HAMAMELIDACEAE

SCIENTIFIC NAME:
Hamamelis virginiana L.

STATUS:
Uncommon but not listed
Edge of geographical range

POSSIBLE LOCATIONS:
Carter County
Iron County
Madison County
Reynolds County
Shannon County—Current River Natural Area
Stoddard County

HABITAT:
Moist woods

DESCRIPTION:

Flowering time:
September-December.

Flower:
Yellow, on short pedicles; **petals 1.5-2 cm long,** fragrant; **calyx lobes brownish-yellow, yellow-green** inside.

Leaves:
5-15 cm long; wavy-toothed; broadly obovate, inequilateral at rounded base; in autumn leaves turn pale to rich yellow or yellow tinged with orange.

Stem:
Shrubs or small tree up to 5 m tall; not suckering; **twigs glabrous or slightly hairy.**

WOODLAND
Hamamelis virginiana

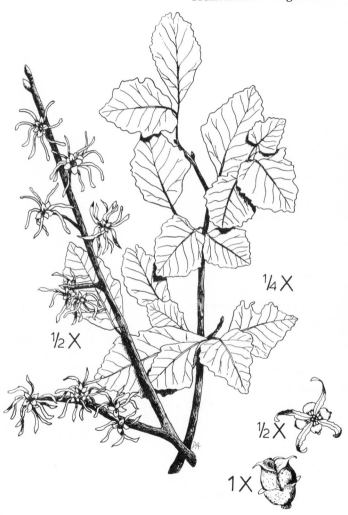

¼ X

½ X

½ X

1 X

BARREN STRAWBERRY

FAMILY:
ROSACEAE

SCIENTIFIC NAME:
Waldsteinia fragarioides (Michx.) Tratt.

STATUS:
Missouri list - rare (relic)

POSSIBLE LOCATIONS:
Dallas County—north-facing wooded bluffs along Niangua River, T.34N., R.18W., Sec. 8, 1½ miles south of Windyville

Douglas County—upland pine-oak wooded slopes east of Bryant Creek, SE of Sweden
—limestone ledges of north-facing bluffs along Little Indian Creek, T.27N., R.11W., SW ¼, Sec. 24 and SE ¼, Sec. 23, 7 miles SE of Ann

Texas County—above limestone bluffs along Jack's Fork of Current River, 5 miles SE of Arroll
—1 mile downstream from Harlow Ford, 4½ miles SE of Arroll

HABITAT:
Moist or dry woods

DESCRIPTION:

Flowering time:
April-May; perennial.

Flower:
Yellow; on a slender, 3-8 flowered, erect scape; petals 5-10 mm long and 3-6 mm broad.

Leaves:
Leaves and petioles 1-2 dm long; 3 leaflets with **unequal, irregular teeth; leaflets wedge-shaped and narrowed to the base;** evergreen.

Stem:
Low growing; stout.

WOODLAND
Waldsteinia fragarioides

½X   1X   ½X

SNOW WREATH

FAMILY:
ROSACEAE

SCIENTIFIC NAME:
Neviusia alabamensis A. Gray

STATUS:
National list - threatened

POSSIBLE LOCATIONS:
Butler County

HABITAT:
Woods

DESCRIPTION:

Flowering time:
April

Flower:
1-4 at tip of pedicel; many white stamens sur-rounded by 5 spreading to reflexed **green, white,** or **greenish-white calyx lobes; no petals.**

Leaves:
Green into late November; thin; doubly serrate.

Stem:
9-18 dm tall; shrubs; grows in clumps.

Fruit:
2-4 **fleshy** drupe-like small ovoid achenes.

½ X

3/2 X

1X

YELLOWWOOD

FAMILY:
LEGUMINOSAE

SCIENTIFIC NAME:
Cladrastis lutea (Michx. f.) K. Koch

STATUS:
Missouri list - rare

POSSIBLE LOCATIONS:
Along White River and tributaries
Barry County—west of Sugar Camp Tower
Stone County
Taney County

HABITAT:
Rich woods and limestone bluffs

DESCRIPTION:

Flowering time:
May-June.

Flower:
White; racemes drooping from the ends of branches.

Leaves:
Pinnately compound leaves of **7-11 leaflets; leaflets 6-13 cm long; some or all of the leaflets pointed at tip; topmost leaflet noticeably broadest at or above the middle.**

Stem:
Tree, up to 17 m high; smooth bark; yellow wood.

Fruit:
Legume 7.5-10 cm long.

WOODLAND
Cladrastis lutea

3/4 X

3/8 X

1/2 X

BLACK SNAKEROOT

FAMILY:
UMBELLIFERAE

SCIENTIFIC NAME:
Sanicula smallii Bickn.

STATUS:
Missouri list - undetermined

POSSIBLE LOCATIONS:
Ripley County

HABITAT:
Rich woods

DESCRIPTION:

Flowering time:
May-June; biennial or perennial.

Flower:
Greenish, greenish-yellow, or greenish-white; sessile; **styles longer than the calyx.**

Leaves:
3 palmately arranged leaflets; lateral leaflets usually deeply lobed; leaflets coarsely toothed.

Stem:
3-7.5 dm high.

Fruit:
5-6 mm long; sessile.

Roots:
Tuberous; thickened.

WOODLAND
Sanicula smallii

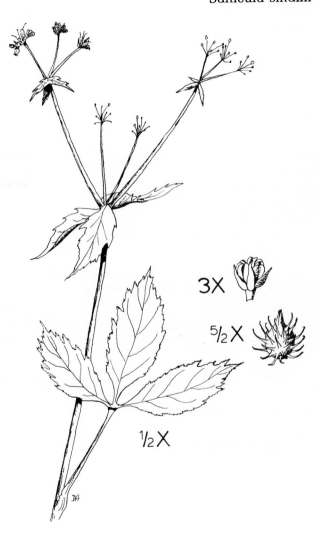

3X

5/2 X

1/2 X

DH

STAGGER-BUSH

FAMILY:
ERICACEAE

SCIENTIFIC NAME:
Lyonia mariana (L.) DC

STATUS:
Missouri list - endangered (relic)

POSSIBLE LOCATIONS:
Dent County—sandy pine-oak woods, T.35N.,
R.7W., Sec. 15 and 16, 2 miles south of Lake
Spring

HABITAT:
Moist, sandy soil; pinelands and open woods

DESCRIPTION:

Flowering time:
May-June

Flower:
White to rose; **corolla 8-13 mm long;** umbelli-
form clusters not subtended by leaves; long-pedi-
celled, nodding.

Leaves:
2-8 cm long; borne on new shoots; deciduous;
elliptic to oblong; entire; hairy on the veins
underneath.

Stem:
Shrub up to 5 m; slender; usually with stems
naked below.

½ X

³⁄₂ X

LOW-BUSH BLUEBERRY

FAMILY:
ERICACEAE

SCIENTIFIC NAME:
Vaccinium vacillans var. *missouriense* Ashe

STATUS:
National list - threatened

POSSIBLE LOCATIONS:
Barton County—upland woods along top of sandstone ledge, 3½ miles NE of Milford
Dade County—along partially shaded sandstone ledges near Turnback Creek, 4 miles east of Greenfield
Ozark County—rocky glades near Tecumseh
Shannon County—slopes of mountain opposite Bee Bluff, along Current River, north of Eminence

HABITAT:
Dry open woods, thickets, and clearings

DESCRIPTION:

Flowering time:
April-May

Flower:
White or greenish, often red-tinged; **barrel-shaped;** in racemes; grows on terminating branchlets or from old axils; flowering when leaves are partly grown; **no bracts present at base of flower stalk.**

Leaves:
2-4 cm long and 1-2 cm wide; oval or elliptic; pale or dull; glaucous beneath.

Stem:
3-9 dm high; without hairs; greenish or brown-tinged branches.

Fruit:
Black berries without bloom.

Vaccinium vacillans var. missouriense

½X

2X

1X

FRINGE TREE

FAMILY:
OLEACEAE

SCIENTIFIC NAME:
Chionanthus virginica L.

STATUS:
Missouri list - rare

POSSIBLE LOCATIONS:
Cape Girardeau County
Douglas County—along Fox Creek T.25N.,
  R.13W., Sec. 21-28.
Mississippi County
Ozark County
Taney County—White River and tributaries

HABITAT:
Rich wet woods, thickets, glades, and bluffs

DESCRIPTION:

Flowering time:
April-May

Flower:
White: on slender pedicels; petals 2-2.5 cm long,
linear; flowers in drooping sprays.

Leaves:
8-15 cm long; **lower surface of leaves, petioles
and young twigs hairy,** or sometimes glabrous;
oval, oblong or obovate-lanceolate; autumn
foliage is pale to rich yellow.

Stem:
Tall shrub or small tree to 10 m.

Fruit:
Purple drupe with a bloom.

½X

1X

½X

MARSH PINK

GENTIANACEAE

SCIENTIFIC NAME:
Sabatia brachiata Ell.

STATUS:
Missouri list - endangered

POSSIBLE LOCATIONS:
Butler County—upland oak-hickory woods, 12 miles north of Poplar Bluff, north of Rombauer, T.26N., R.7E., Sec. 20, near head of Mud Creek

HABITAT:
Dry or moist soil, pinelands, oak-woods, and clearings

DESCRIPTION:

Flowering time:
June-August; annual.

Flower:
Pink with a yellow or green eye or rarely white; flower both clustered and solitary at tips of branchlets.

Leaves:
1.5-4 cm long; sessile; lanceolate to narrowly oblong or linear; narrowed at base, **not clasping.**

Stem:
1.5-6 dm high; slender; few opposite erect branches beyond the middle; **angles of stem without wings.**

WOODLAND
Sabatia brachiata

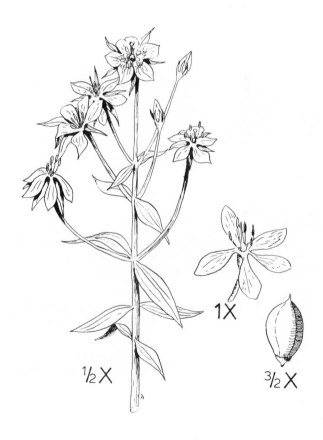

½ X

1 X

³/2 X

CLIMBING MILKWEED

FAMILY:
ASCLEPIADACEAE

SCIENTIFIC NAME:
Matelea obliqua (Jacq.) Woodson

STATUS:
Missouri list - rare

POSSIBLE LOCATIONS:
Howell County
Madison County
St. Louis County
Shannon County

HABITAT:
Rocky woods and thickets

DESCRIPTION:

Flowering time:
May-June

Flower:
Greenish-brown outside and purple inside; **all the lobes of the crown truncate;** in a many flowered umbel; buds cone-shaped.

Leaves:
Rounded to cordate-ovate; leaves pointed at tip; pubescent.

Stem:
Climbing or twining; pubescent.

1/2 X

1/7 X

CAROLINA PHLOX

FAMILY:

POLEMONIACEAE

SCIENTIFIC NAME:

Phlox carolina L.

STATUS:

Missouri list - undetermined

Edge of geographical range

POSSIBLE LOCATIONS:

Carter County—Big Barren Creek

HABITAT:

Wet to dry open woods, thickets, and clearings

DESCRIPTION:

Flowering time:

May-July; perennial.

Flower:

Bright red-purple to pink (rarely white); petals 1-1.4 cm long; **sepals narrow with a midrib.**

Leaves:

4-10 cm long; **largest leaves in upper half of stem; lanceolate to ovate-oblong;** glabrous or nearly so.

Stem:

2-7.5 dm high; either several in a crown or scattered from axils of old branches; glabrous or nearly so.

WOODLAND
Phlox carolina

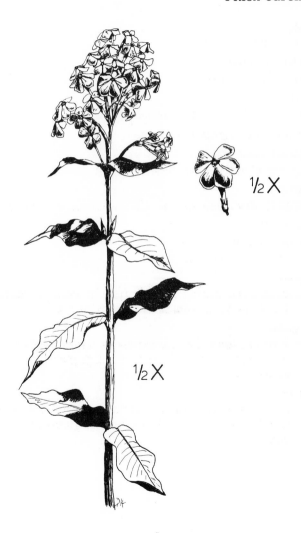

½ X

½ X

FRENCH MULBERRY

FAMILY:
VERBENACEAE

SCIENTIFIC NAME:
Callicarpa americana L.

STATUS:
Missouri list - possibly extirpated

Edge of geographical range

POSSIBLE LOCATIONS:
Taney County—White River and tributaries

HABITAT:
Moist wooded areas

DESCRIPTION:

Flowering time:
June-August

Flower:
Bluish to reddish (white rare); in many-flowered cymes located in axils of leaves.

Leaves:
8-23 cm long and 3.5-13 cm wide; opposite; ovate-oblong, tapering base, pointed tip, toothed; whitish-tomentose beneath.

Stem:
Shrub; 0.5-2 m high; twigs densely tomentose.

Fruit:
Pinkish or violet color; densely clustered in the axils of leaves.

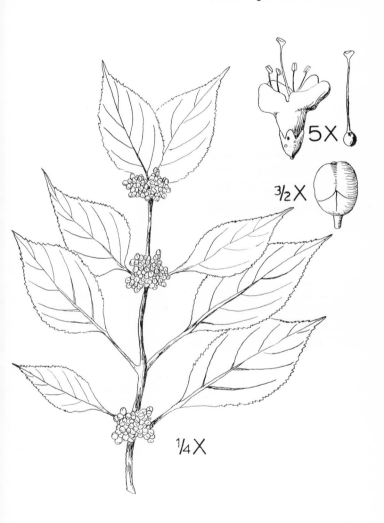

WOODLAND
Callicarpa americana

5X

3/2 X

1/4 X

SKULLCAP

FAMILY:
LABIATAE

SCIENTIFIC NAME:
Scutellaria serrata Andr. var. *montana* (Chapm.)
Penland

STATUS:
Missouri list - endangered

POSSIBLE LOCATIONS:
Iron County

HABITAT:
Rich woods and bluffs

DESCRIPTION:

Flowering time:
May-June; perennial

Flower:
Blue; abruptly upcurved from base; **lowest pair of flowers subtended by foliage leaves; corolla 2.5-3.5 cm long; upper side of the calyx shaped like the seat of a tractor.**

Leaves:
5-11 cm long; 4-6 pairs; **glandular-pubescent;** ovate-oblong, pointed at tip, toothed; **leaves from upper part of the stem are the largest.**

Stem:
2-7 dm high; square; 1-few from a firm base; slender; **glandular-pubescent.**

WOODLAND
Scutellaria serrata var. montana

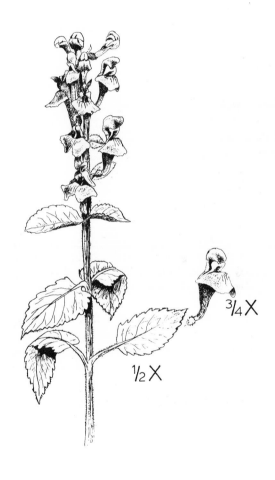

³⁄₄ X

½ X

HORSEMINT
or WILD BERGAMONT

FAMILY:
LABIATAE

SCIENTIFIC NAME:
Monarda clinopodia L.

STATUS:
Missouri list - rare
Edge of geographical range

POSSIBLE LOCATIONS:
Butler County—rich wooded valley just below junction of the 2 forks of West Prong and East Prong of Indian Creek, T.25N., R.6E., NE ¼ Sec. 1 and NW ¼ Sec. 6, 6½ miles NNE of Poplar Bluff

HABITAT:
Woods, thickets, and streambanks

DESCRIPTION:

Flowering time:
Late June-July; perennial.

Flower:
Corolla dull white to flesh pink with dark spots, 1.5-3 cm long; calyx 6-10 mm long with a **beard of hairs in the throat**; 1 flower-cluster at the top of the stem; **bracts at base of flower-cluster white or white-tinged.**

Leaves:
6-12 cm long; dark green; petioled; thin and membranous; cordate-ovate to ovate-lanceolate; bracts at base of flower cluster white or white-tinged.

Stem:
0.5-1.5 m high; square; slender.

WOODLAND
Monarda clinopodia

$^{3}/_{4}$ X

$^{1}/_{2}$ X

MOUNTAIN MINT

FAMILY:
LABIATAE

SCIENTIFIC NAME:
Pycnanthemum muticum (Michx.) Pers.

STATUS:
Missouri list - rare

POSSIBLE LOCATIONS:
Butler County
Dunklin County

HABITAT:
Dry or moist woods, meadows, thickets and clearings

DESCRIPTION:

Flowering time:
July-September; perennial.

Flower:
Corolla purple to white, lower lip purple-spotted; small flowers in crowded, head-like cymes 8-15 mm wide, solitary at tips of branches.

Leaves:
4-7 cm long; ovate to broadly ovate-lanceolate, pointed at tip, **rounded at base, toothed with 5-10 teeth on each margin; bracts under flower cluster whitened with velvety pubescence.**

Stem:
4-8 dm; square branched above with short hairs.

WOODLAND
Pycnanthemum muticum

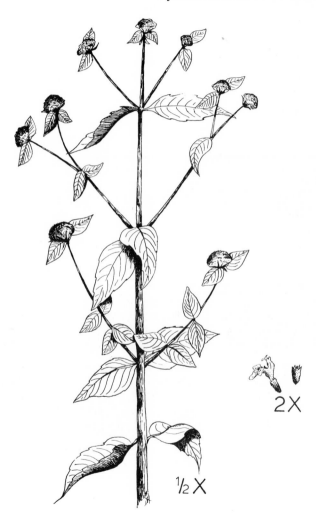

2X

½ X

65

LIMBER HONEYSUCKLE

FAMILY:
CAPRIFOLIACEAE

SCIENTIFIC NAME:
Lonicera dioica L.

STATUS:
Missouri status - rare

POSSIBLE LOCATIONS:
Boone County

Dent County—hanging over and near top of north-facing limestone bluffs along Spring branch from Montauk Spring, Montauk State Park.

—on north-facing bluffs along creek tributary to Crooked Creek, Montauk State Park.

HABITAT:
Moist or dry woods, thickets, rocky banks, and bluffs

DESCRIPTION:

Flowering time:
April-June

Flower:
1.5-2.5 cm long; greenish-yellow **tinged with purple, rose, or brick color**; flowers in 1-3 crowded whorls; outside of flower without hair, inside is pubescent.

Leaves:
4-10 cm long; oblong or elliptic; short-petioled or subsessile; green above, **glaucous beneath;** lower surface without hairs; upper 1-4 pairs joined at their bases.

Stem:
Climbing shrub without hairs or branches.

WOODLAND
Lonicera dioica

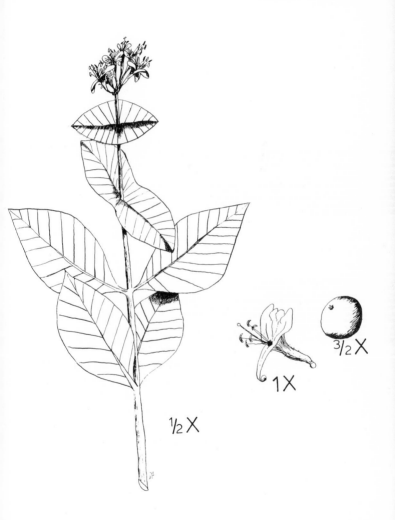

1/2 X

1X

3/2 X

HAREBELL or BLUEBELL

FAMILY:
CAMPANULACEAE

SCIENTIFIC NAME:
Campanula rotundifolia L.

STATUS:
Missouri list - endangered (relic)

POSSIBLE LOCATIONS:
Shannon County—along Jack's Fork, Jam-up Bluff, 7 miles north of Montier

HABITAT:
Dry woods, meadows, bluffs, and open or rocky banks

DESCRIPTION:

Flowering time:
May-August; perennial

Flower:
13-27 mm long; purplish-blue; bell-shaped, lobes much shorter than the tube; 1-15 flowers on long stalks or loosely flowered inflorescence.

Leaves:
Basal leaves (rarely present at flowering time) are round-cordate to ovate, mostly toothed, long-petioled; cauline leaves numerous, linear or narrowly lanceolate, **smooth.**

Stem:
1-8 dm; **slender; upper half without hairs.**

WOODLAND
Campanula rotundifolia

³⁄₄ X

½ X

HYSSOP—LEAVED THOROUGHWORT

FAMILY:

COMPOSITAE

SCIENTIFIC NAME:

Eupatorium hyssopifolium L. var *calcaratum* Fern. and Schub.

STATUS:

Missouri list - endangered (relic)

POSSIBLE LOCATIONS:

Howell County—bordering Twin Ponds, east of Highway A, T.23N., R.8W., NW ¼ Sec. 16, 4 miles south of West Plains

HABITAT:

Dry, open woods and clearings

DESCRIPTION:

Flowering time:

August-November; perennial

Flower:

White; flattish-topped corymb; flower-heads 3-7 flowered.

Leaves:

3.5-6 cm long; primary **narrowly linear;** entire or with revolute margins; frequently in threes; bearing spurs from the axillary clusters of leaves; **base of leaves tapering.**

Stem:

0.3-1.4 dm high; often clustered.

Eupatorium hyssopifolium var. calcaratum

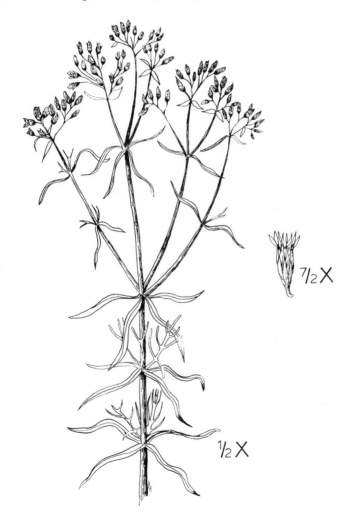

7/2 X

½ X

71

OTHER PLANTS SOMETIMES FOUND
IN WOODLANDS

GLADE SPECIES

ASHE JUNIPER

FAMILY:
CUPRESSACEAE

SCIENTIFIC NAME:
Juniperus ashei Bushholz

STATUS:
Uncommon but not listed

Edge of geographical range

POSSIBLE LOCATIONS:
Along bluffs and glades of the White River and
  tributaries
Barry County
Ozark County
Stone County
Taney County

HABITAT:
Limestone glades and bald knobs

DESCRIPTION:

Leaves:
Scale-like and toothed when viewed with a lens;
leaves often have a conspicuous dorsal gland.

Fruit:
6-8.5 mm long; copper-colored to dark blue
berry with a dense bloom; has 1 seed (rarely 2 or
3) per berry that is 4-5.8 mm long; **pointed,
without pits, but with a conspicuous white
growth.**

Trunk:
Bushy tree with **several trunks from one base**
forming an irregular or rounded head 2-6 m
high.

GLADE
Juniperus ashei

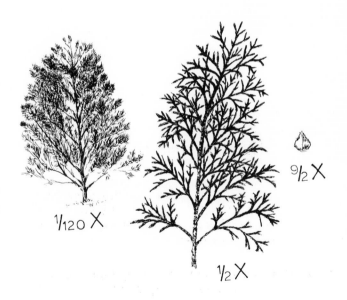

1/120 X

1/2 X

9/2 X

REED BENT GRASS

FAMILY:
GRAMINEAE

SCIENTIFIC NAME:
Calamagrostis insperata Swallen

STATUS:
National list - endangered

Missouri list - endangered

Edge of geographical range

POSSIBLE LOCATIONS:
Douglas County—rocky, grassy, open, cherty lime-
stone slopes at east end of bluffs along Indian
Creek, near Holy Cliff, 3½ miles NE of Topaz
Ozark County—lower chert slopes in Blue Springs
Game Refuge, Mark Twain National Forest

HABITAT:
Wooded ravines and open slopes of bluffs

DESCRIPTION:

Flowering time:
June-September; perennial

Flower:
Panicle with spreading branches in several
whorls; **spikelets 5 mm long;** glumes nearly
equal; lemma with tufts of short hairs from the
sides; **awn of lemma bent near the middle and
twisted near the base.**

Leaves:
Leaf blades 4-8 mm wide; long tapering; sheaths
without hairs; ligule conspicuous.

Stem:
1 m tall; rhizomatous.

GLADE
Calamagrostis insperata

5X   ¼X

BALD GRASS

FAMILY:
GRAMINEAE

SCIENTIFIC NAME:
Sporobolus neglectus var. *ozarkanus* (Fern.)
Steyerm. and Kucera

STATUS:
National list - threatened
Missouri list - rare

POSSIBLE LOCATIONS:
Barton County
Jasper County—barrens, Webb City
Lawrence County—limestone ledge, open or partly
wooded hillside, near Verona
Ozark County—slopes and ledges, bald knobs,
"Bald Jesse" near Gainesville

HABITAT:
Limestone glades, dry woods and waste ground

DESCRIPTION:

Flowering time:
July-August, annual

Flower:
Panicles crowded, 2-4 cm long, inserted in
sheaths; **spikelets 3.5-5 mm long; glumes about
equal,** shorter than the florets; lemma and palea
plump, glabrous.

Leaves:
Leaf-blades with hairs; **sheaths inflated**; lower
**leaf-sheaths and blades have hairs with swellings
at base.**

Stem:
Prostrate at base; branching from base to 50 cm
tall; in tufts.

GLADE
Sporobolus neglectus var. ozarkanus

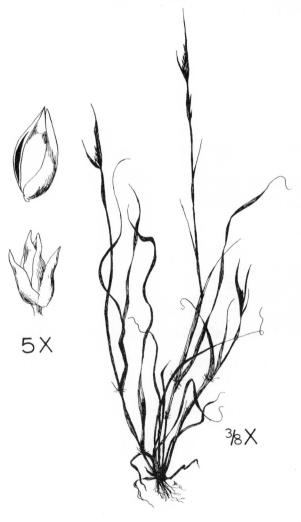

5 X

3/8 X

DEATH CAMAS

FAMILY:
LILIACEAE

SCIENTIFIC NAME:
Zigadenus nuttallii Gray

STATUS:
Missouri list - rare

Edge of geographical range

POSSIBLE LOCATIONS:
Oregon County—"The Narrows" on a dry narrow limestone open wooded ridge on a glade above a bluff above Blue Spring along Fredericks Fork, west of Calm.

HABITAT:
Prairies and calcareous rocks, glades.

DESCRIPTION:

Flowering time:
May; perennial

Flower:
Yellowish-white; **sepals and petals 6-8 mm long,** oval, each with an unlobed obovate basal gland.

Leaves:
3 dm long and 10 mm wide; present at time of flowering or fruiting; main leaves arise at base of plant; falcate.

Stem:
3-7.5 dm high; stout; plant is poisonous.

Roots:
Bulb; outer bulb-coats papery, not fibrous.

GLADE
Zigadenus nuttallii

1 X

¼ X

81

SOAPWEED

FAMILY:
LILIACEAE
SCIENTIFIC NAME:
Yucca glauca var. *mollis* Engelm.

STATUS:
Missouri list - rare
Edge of geographical range

POSSIBLE LOCATIONS:
Barry County—along west and southwest side of White River, T.21N., R.26W., Sec. 28 and SW Sec. 21, 3-3½ miles south of Eagle Rock
Oregon County
Ozark County
Stone County
Taney County

HABITAT:
Glades, rocky wooded slopes, and banks along streams in limestone soils

DESCRIPTION:
Flowering time:
May-June
Flower:
3.5-7 cm long; greenish-white in general but the sepals show a tinge of purplish-pink over their whole surface and have a broad greenish-white margin; **petals and sepals blunt at tip** with the petals being longer and broader than the sepals; flower-stalk is unbranched.
Leaves:
1-2.5 cm broad; linear; **soft and flexible**; have thread-like fibers separating loose from the margins; main leaves arising at plant base.
Stems:
Short; woody.
Fruit:
A capsule; **seeds 8-10 mm long** and black.

1/8 X

3/8 X

1/4 X

1/4 X

UMBRELLA PLANT

FAMILY:

POLYGONACEAE

SCIENTIFIC NAME:

Eriogonum longifolium Nutt.

STATUS:

Missouri list - endangered (one of the rarest plants in Missouri)

Edge of geographical range

POSSIBLE LOCATIONS:

Oregon County

Ozark County—west-facing bald knob along North Fork of White River, T.21N., R. 12W., Sec. 2 between Pumphrey Ford and White Ferry, 1½ miles south of Udall.

Taney County—limestone bluffs along White River, T.21N., R.19W., Sec. 7, 2 miles south of Groom, 4-5 miles south of Cedar Creek.

HABITAT:

Glades, rocky woods and bluffs

DESCRIPTION:

Flowering time:

July-October; perennial

Flower:

Yellow-green; in clusters **subtended by a hairy, gray-white involucre.**

Leaves:

Basal rosette of long narrow leaves that are dull olive green on the upper side and have **dense, velvety gray-white hairs below;** rosette persists over winter; 3-4 scattered leaves on stem.

Stem:

1.5-1.65 m tall; **gray-white hairy; single stem branches at flowers.**

GLADE
Eriogonum longifolium

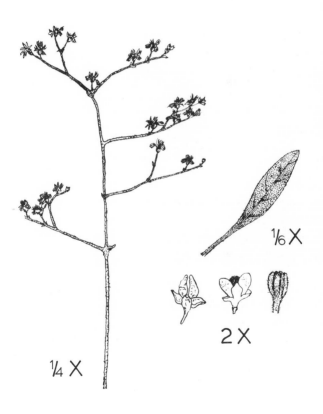

¹⁄₆ X

¹⁄₄ X

2 X

JOINTWEED

FAMILY:
POLYGONACEAE

SCIENTIFIC NAME:
Polygonella americana (Fisch. and Mey.) Small

STATUS:
Missouri list - rare

POSSIBLE LOCATIONS:
Dunklin County
Iron County
Scott County
Stoddard County

HABITAT:
Dry, sandy ground

DESCRIPTION:

Flowering time:
July-October; perennial

Flower:
White to pink tinged; **in racemes.**

Leaves:
Small; **linear**; gray-green.

Stem:
3-12 dm high; shrubby, branches low and spreading.

GLADE
Polygonella americana

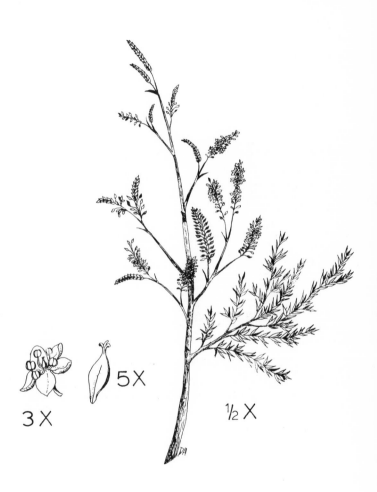

3 X

5 X

½ X

87

FOUR O'CLOCK

FAMILY:
NYCTAGINACEAE

SCIENTIFIC NAME:
Mirabilis linearis (Pursh.) Heimerl.

STATUS:
Missouri list - rare

POSSIBLE LOCATIONS:
Jackson County
Jasper County
Lawrence County
Maries County
Miller County

HABITAT:
Dry open soils, rocky prairies, and glades

DESCRIPTION:

Flowering time:
May-October; perennial

Flower:
Pink to purple; 3-5 in number; has a short tube.

Leaves:
5-15 mm wide; **linear**; thick and glaucous.

Stem:
Tall; **without hairs below inflorescence.**

Fruit:
Angles smooth.

GLADE
Mirabilis linearis

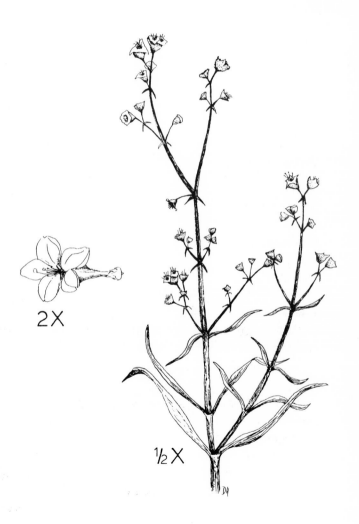

2X

½X

89

GEOCARPON

FAMILY:
CARYOPHYLLACEAE

SCIENTIFIC NAME:
Geocarpon minimum Mackenzie

STATUS:
National list - endangered
Missouri list - endangered

POSSIBLE LOCATIONS:
Southwest Missouri
Dade County
Greene County
Jasper County
Polk County
St. Clair County

HABITAT:
Sandstone glades

DESCRIPTION:

Flowering time:
Early April-May; annual

Flower:
Petals absent; perianth is pale green with the lower part frequently tinged with wine-purplish color.

Leaves:
Larger leaves about 5 mm long; narrowly oblong or ovate-oblong and **are blunt at tip;** no stipules at the base of leaves.

Stem:
1-4 cm tall; more or less erect; dull wine-purplish throughout or at maturity may turn an inconspicuous dull gray-green color; overall succulent aspect.

GLADE
Geocarpon minimum

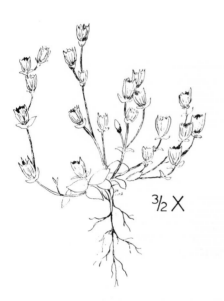

³/₂ X

3 X

TRELEASE'S LARKSPUR

FAMILY:

RANUNCULACEAE

SCIENTIFIC NAME:

Delphinium treleasei Bush

STATUS:

National list - threatened

POSSIBLE LOCATIONS:

Barry County—rocky slopes and ledges, bald knobs near Eagle Rock

—Highway 86 about 5-7 miles east of junction with No. 112, NE or Roaring River State Park

Cedar County

Dade County

Greene County

Lawrence County

Polk County

Stone County

Taney County—by Highway 65, 6 miles north of Branson

HABITAT:

Limestone glades and bald knobs

DESCRIPTION:

Flowering time:

May-June

Flower:

Deep blue or deep purple (rarely white); yellow and brown spots on sepals; petals with a conspicuous yellow beard 2.5-3.7 cm long; **pedicels over 2.5 cm long.**

Leaves:

Mostly basal; deep leaf divisions, **divisions narrow and linear;** 1-3 small leaves on stem.

Stem:

5-20 dm high; slender; **without hairs.**

Seeds:

Covered with a loose, wrinkled coat.

GLADE
Delphinium treleasei

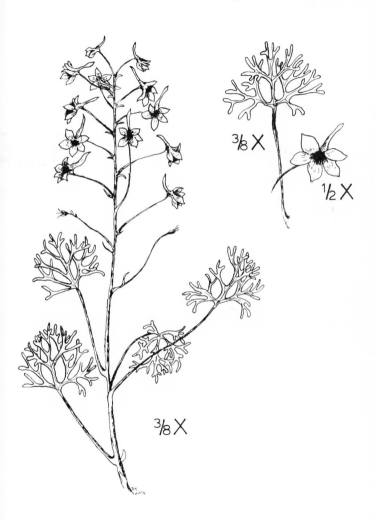

$^3/_8$ X

$^1/_2$ X

$^3/_8$ X

AMERICAN BARBERRY

FAMILY:

BERBERIDACEAE

SCIENTIFIC NAME:

Berberis canadensis Mill.

STATUS:

Missouri list - rare

Edge of geographical range

POSSIBLE LOCATIONS:

Howell County—"County Hollow" by the bluffs of Eleven Points River, about 5 miles NE of Peace Valley

Shannon County—top of Jam-up Bluff along Jack's Fork of Current River

Texas County—between Barn Hollow Canyon and Highway 17 along Jack's Fork of Current River

HABITAT:

Dry woodlands and bluffs

DESCRIPTION:

Flowering time:

May; perennial

Fruiting time:

June-July

Flower:

Yellow; **petals entire;** racemes 2-4 cm, with 5-10 flowers on pedicels.

Leaves:

2-6 cm long; toothed; **teeth of mature leaves not ending in bristle.**

Stem:

1-2 m; shrub; sparsely branched; **younger twigs purple, brown or reddish;** most prickles forked or 3-branched.

Fruit:

A red, juicy berry.

Wood:

Yellow.

GLADE
Berberis canadensis

1X

2X

½ X

BLADDER-POD

FAMILY:
CRUCIFERAE

SCIENTIFIC NAME:
Lesquerella filiformis Rollins

STATUS:
National list - endangered

POSSIBLE LOCATIONS:
Dade County
Greene County
Jasper County
Lawrence County

HABITAT:
Limestone glades, barrens, and rocky open woods

DESCRIPTION:

Flowering time:
April-May; annual

Flower:
Yellow; 5-20 on a pedicel

Leaves:
Alternate except for rosette at base; **silvery;** not clasping; rosette leaves are entire and sparsely pubescent; cauline leaves 5-10 in number, linear, entire.

Stem:
1-2.5 dm high, **slender, silvery.**

Fruit:
Round, without hairs, **sessile.**

GLADE
Lesquerella filiformis

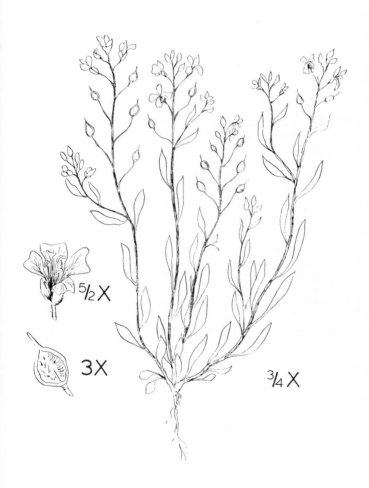

5/2 X

3X

3/4 X

97

MISSOURI ALUMROOT

FAMILY:
SAXIFRAGACEAE

SCIENTIFIC NAME:
Heuchera missouriensis Rosendahl.

STATUS:
National list - endangered (endemic)

Missouri list - endangered

POSSIBLE LOCATIONS:
Madison County—along St. Francis River near
Jewett

Wayne County—along St. Francis River, 5 miles
south of Kime

HABITAT:
Limestone bluffs

DESCRIPTION:

Flowering time:
July-August; perennial

Flower:
White; petals 1.5 mm long; **calyx covered with
long, spreading, gland-tipped hairs.**

Leaves:
Basal; lower surface hairy; resembles leaf of
cultivated geranium.

GLADE
Heuchera missouriensis

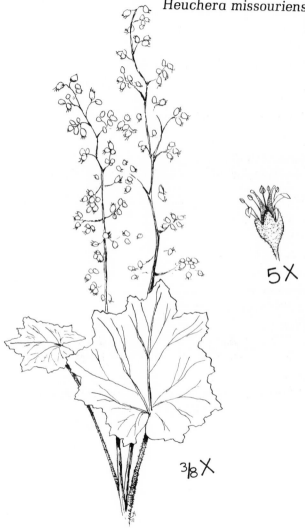

5X

3/8 X

GOLDEN CURRANT

FAMILY:
SAXIFRAGACEAE

SCIENTIFIC NAME:
Ribes odoratum Wendland f.

STATUS:
Missouri list - status undetermined
Edge of geographical range

POSSIBLE LOCATIONS:
Along the White River and tributaries and Jack's
Fork of the Current River
Barry County
Shannon County—west-facing bluffs, T.29N.,
R.4W., west ½ Sec. 25, 1 mile NE of Eminence
—south-facing bluffs T.29N.,
R.3W., north of Sec. 20, 4½ miles NE of
Eminence
Stone County
Taney County

HABITAT:
Rocky bluffs and slopes

DESCRIPTION:

Flowering time:
April-June; perennial

Fruiting time:
June-August

Flower:
Golden-yellow; fragrant; calyx tube 3-4 times
longer than the oval lobes.

Leaves:
3-5 lobed; **pale green;** lobes entire in their lower
half, often few-toothed above.

Stem:
A tall, **spineless** shrub.

Fruit:
A black or rarely yellow berry.

GLADE
Ribes odoratum

3/4 X

1 X

3/4 X

DH

HAIRLESS LEADPLANT

FAMILY:
LEGUMINOSAE

SCIENTIFIC NAME:
Amorpha brachycarpa Palmer

STATUS:
National list - threatened (endemic)

Missouri list - rare

POSSIBLE LOCATIONS:
Barry County—glade south of Roaring River Park
Lawrence County—open limestone bank, border of
    woods, near Bonham Siding
Stone County—Galena

HABITAT:
Rocky open woods and glades

DESCRIPTION:

Flowering time:
May-August

Flower:
Blue

Leaves:
Nearly sessile; compound with odd number of
leaflets that are 4-8 mm wide and rarely more
than 17 mm long.

Stem:
Low, shrubby plants, less than 1 m tall; **without
hairs** or nearly so.

Fruit:
Conspicuously **resin-dotted**; glabrous.

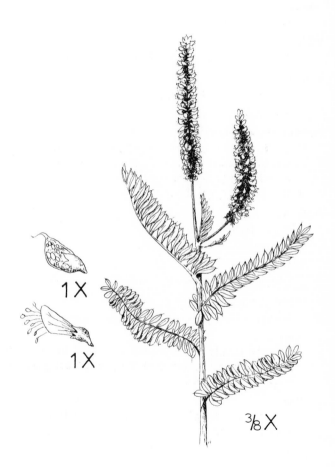

1 X

1 X

$\frac{3}{8}$ X

SPURGE

FAMILY:
EUPHORBIACEAE

SCIENTIFIC NAME:
Phyllanthus polygonoides Nutt.

STATUS:
Missouri list - undetermined

POSSIBLE LOCATIONS:
Stone County—limestone barren in upland cedar area, T.22N., R.24W., Sec. 18, 4 miles east of Shell Knob

HABITAT:
Limestone glades

DESCRIPTION:

Flowering time:
June-October; perennial

Flower:
Creamy or creamy-greenish color; petals absent.

Leaves:
Gray-green above, silvery beneath; ascending; without teeth, **oblanceolate.**

Stems:
Woody low shrub, grows in bunches with ascending stems; without hairs; without milky juice.

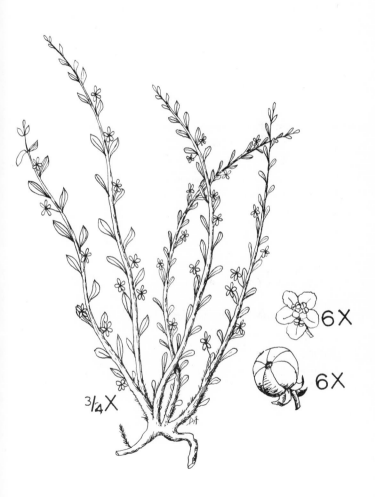

3/4X

6X

6X

POPPY-MALLOW

FAMILY:

MALVACEAE

SCIENTIFIC NAME:

Callirhoe papaver var. *bushii* (Fern.) Waterfall

STATUS:

National list - threatened

Missouri list - rare

POSSIBLE LOCATIONS:

Barry County
McDonald County
Ozark County
Stone County
Taney County

HABITAT:

Rocky woods, glades, prairies, and roadsides

DESCRIPTION:

Flowering time:

May-August

Flower:

Deep rose, rose-red, purple or rose-purple; 3
bractlets present at base of calyx.

Leaves:

Some parts of leaves entire; **leaves deeply lobed
or parted;** stipules prominent.

Stem:

Hairy, **hairs pointing toward base of plant; erect.**

³⁄₈ X

³⁄₈ X

BUSHY ST. JOHN'S-WORT

FAMILY:
HYPERICACEAE

SCIENTIFIC NAME:
Hypericum densiflorum Pursh.

STATUS:
Missouri list - undetermined

POSSIBLE LOCATIONS:
Madison County
Ripley County
Taney County

HABITAT:
Wet or dry sandy soil

DESCRIPTION:

Flowering time:
July-September

Flower:
Yellow; numerous in crowded cymes; mainly terminal; **3 styles, sepals 2-5 mm long.**

Leaves:
2-4 cm long and 5-8 mm wide; dark green; crowded; thickish; linear.

Stem:
Shrub up to 2 m; much branched above.

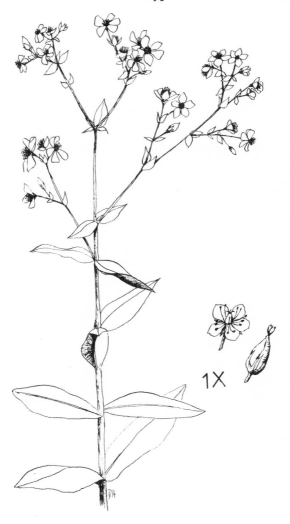

1X

FLAX-LEAVED STENOSIPHON

FAMILY:
ONAGRACEAE

SCIENTIFIC NAME:
Stenosiphon linifolius (Nutt.) Britt.

STATUS:
Missouri list - endangered

POSSIBLE LOCATIONS:
Ozark County
Taney County

HABITAT:
Rocky limestone glades and bald knobs

DESCRIPTION:

Flowering time:
July-October; biennial

Flower:
White; numerous in an elongated spike.

Leaves:
Smooth gray-green; **sessile; glabrous;** narrowly lanceolate to linear, pointed, entire; first year there is a small rosette of leaves produced which overwinter.

Stem:
6-15 dm; slender; **glabrous**; in the 2nd year a single, unbranched stem is sent up.

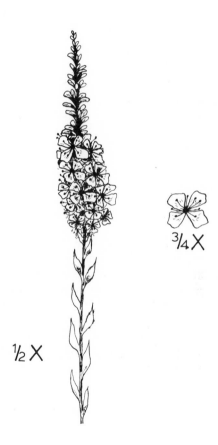

³/₄ X

½ X

CENTAURY

FAMILY:
GENTIANACEAE

SCIENTIFIC NAME:
Centaurium texense (Griseb.) Fern.

STATUS:
Missouri list - rare

Edge of geographical range

POSSIBLE LOCATIONS:
Barry County
Greene County
Hickory County
Miller County
Ozark County
Stone County
Taney County
Webster County

HABITAT:
Limestone glades and bald knobs

DESCRIPTION:

Flowering time:
June to early September

Flower:
Rose purple or reddish; has star-shaped **lobes 4-6 mm long;** corolla-tube very narrow and slender, twice the length of lobes.

Leaves:
1-8 mm broad; pale green; **linear** or narrowly lanceolate; upper leaves reduced to bracts.

Stem:
1-3 dm tall; dwarf; forked.

GLADE
Centaurium texense

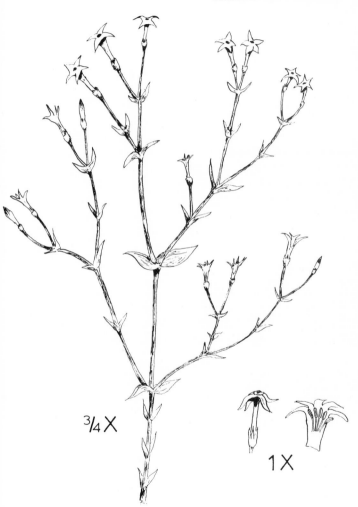

3/4 X

1 X

CILIATE BLUE STAR

FAMILY:
APOCYNACEAE

SCIENTIFIC NAME:
Amsonia ciliata Walt. var. *filifolia* Wood

STATUS:
Missouri list - rare

Edge of geographical range

POSSIBLE LOCATIONS:
Douglas County—North Fork of White River and Bryant Creek
Ozark County

HABITAT:
Glades and bluffs

DESCRIPTION:

Flowering time:
April-May; perennial

Flower:
Pale blue; long peduncle, in dense clusters; no hair on outside of petals.

Leaves:
0.5-5 mm broad; alternate; very numerous, crowded; **narrow, linear.**

Stem:
2-4 dm tall.

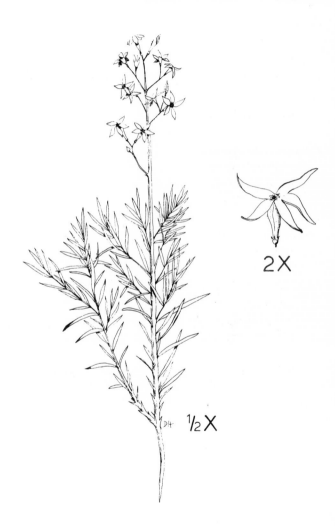

2 X

½ X

MEAD'S MILKWEED

FAMILY:
ASCLEPIADACEAE

SCIENTIFIC NAME:
Asclepias meadii Torr.

STATUS:
National list - endangered

Missouri list - endangered

POSSIBLE LOCATIONS:
Benton County
Cass County
Henry County
Iron County
Johnson County
Pettis County
Polk County
St. Louis County

HABITAT:
Dry prairies and glades

DESCRIPTION:
Flowering time:
May-June; perennial

Flower:
12-14 mm long; **greenish corolla lobes with purplish hoods;** fragrant; single umbel at tip of long peduncle; few flowered.

Leaves:
3-8 cm long; 3-6 pairs; opposite; **cordate-ovate to lanceolate;** sessile; clasping.

Stem:
4-9 dm tall; slender; rarely branched; without hairs; glaucous.

GLADE
Asclepias meadii

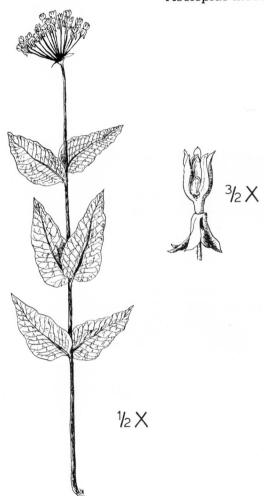

3/2 X

1/2 X

SAND PHLOX

FAMILY:

POLEMONIACEAE

SCIENTIFIC NAME:

Phlox bifida var. *stellaria* (Gray) Wherry

STATUS:

Missouri list - rare

Edge of geographical range

POSSIBLE LOCATIONS:

Douglas County—along Spring Creek near Roosevelt, T.25N., R.11W., Sec. 23

Stone County—along Highway 13 and 86, 4 miles SE of Lampe

Taney County—along Swan Creek, ½ mile NE of Forsyth

HABITAT:

Sandy soil, bluffs, and glades

DESCRIPTION:

Flowering time:

Late March-May; perennial

Flower:

Pale lavender to rose-lavender to white with a purplish tube (or rarely all white); **petals deeply split nearly to or below the middle—appearing almost 10-lobed;** in cymes; few flowered.

Leaves:

2-6 cm long; **1.5-3 mm broad**; linear to very narrow; stiff.

Stem:

1-3 dm tall; **sprawling or trailing** with several erect flowering branches; **no gland-tipped hairs.**

118

GLADE
Phlox bifida var. stellaria

1X

½ X

119

PURPLE BEARD-TONGUE

FAMILY:
SCROPHULARIACEAE

SCIENTIFIC NAME:
Penstemon cobaea var. *purpureus* Pennell

STATUS:
National list - threatened

POSSIBLE LOCATIONS:
Barry County
Christian County
Ozark County
Stone County
Taney County

HABITAT:
Limestone glades and bald knobs

DESCRIPTION:

Flowering time:
April-June; perennial

Flower:
Violet or rose-purple; hairy; corolla 3.5-5 cm long; sepals 7-13 mm long.

Leaves:
10-20 cm long; oblong to narrowly ovate; sharp, short teeth.

Stem:
Up to 7.5 dm high; **finely and minutely hairy.**

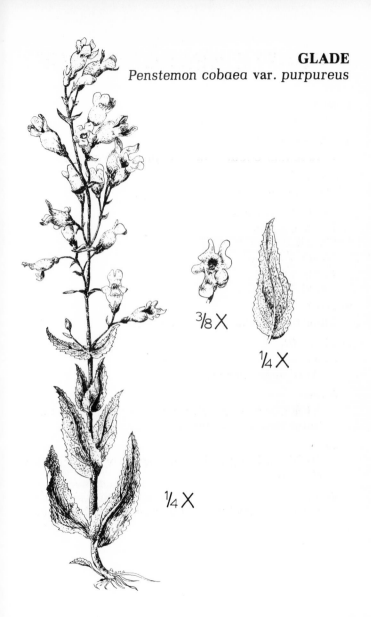

GLADE

Penstemon cobaea var. purpureus

3/8 X

1/4 X

1/4 X

NORTHERN BEDSTRAW

FAMILY:
RUBIACEAE

SCIENTIFIC NAME:
Galium boreale L. var. *hyssopifolium* (Hoffm.)
D.C.

STATUS:
Missouri list - endangered (relic)

POSSIBLE LOCATIONS:
Shannon County—on top of Jam-up Bluff, 6 miles
NW of Montier
Texas County—base of bluffs along Jack's Fork of
Current River, T.27N., R.7W., Sec. 36, 6 miles
SE of Arroll

HABITAT:
Wide variety; not too dry

DESCRIPTION:

Flowering time:
Late May-July; perennial

Flower:
Bright white; in compact terminal panicles.

Leaves:
1.5-5 cm long; **largest leaves 2-5 mm wide;**
linear-lanceolate; in fours; **lower surface
obscurely or not at all marked with narrow pits
or depressions.**

Stem:
3-9 dm high; erect; smooth.

Fruit:
Without hairs.

GLADE
Galium boreale var. hyssopifolium

½ X

5 X

BLAZING STAR

FAMILY:
COMPOSITAE

SCIENTIFIC NAME:
Liatris mucronata D.C.

STATUS:
Missouri list - rare

POSSIBLE LOCATIONS:
Barry County
Christian County
Stone County
Taney County

HABITAT:
Dry, open soil; glades, bald knobs, and bluffs

DESCRIPTION:

Flowering time:
July-October; perennial

Flower:
Pink-purple (white occasionally); **inflorescence
rarely more than 3 dm long;** heads 3-6 flowered;
lobes of corolla without hairs.

Leaves:
Basal leaves 1-5 mm broad; grass green; very
numerous and overlapping; **margins of leaves
without hairs.**

Stem:
1.5-8 dm high; without hairs.

Roots:
A **subglobose corm,** 2-7 cm in diameter.

GLADE
Liatris mucronata

3/4 X

1/2 X

DAISY FLEABANE

FAMILY:

COMPOSITAE

SCIENTIFIC NAME:

Erigeron pusillus Nutt.

STATUS:

Missouri list - endangered

POSSIBLE LOCATIONS:

Ripley County—ravine slopes tributary to Little Black River, between Greenville Ford and Pennington Ford, T.24N., R.3E., Sec. 10, 15, 22, 23, 24, 25, 26, 10-13 miles NE of Doniphan.

HABITAT:

Dry, sandy soil

DESCRIPTION:

Flowering time:

Late June-October

Flower:

Flowers few; heads racemose or cymose on the branches; ray flowers relatively numerous, white to lavender, **bracts with purple tips.**

Leaves:

Lowest obovate to oblong, entire; middle and upper are narrowly linear; leaf surface without hairs; leaf margin has longest hairs near the base, short hairs on the margin nearly to tip.

Stem:

0.5-1 m high; **without hairs, except sometimes at base.**

GLADE
Erigeron pusillus

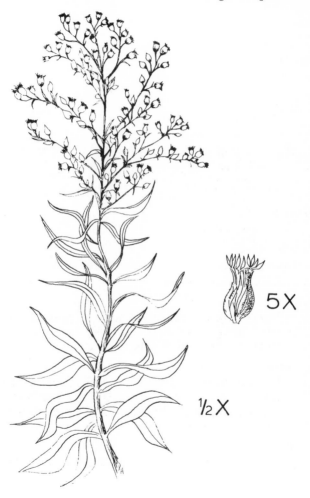

5X

½X

OTHER PLANTS SOMETIMES FOUND IN GLADES, BLUFFS AND ROCKY SLOPES

WET LOWLAND SPECIES

BLUE-EYED GRASS

FAMILY:
IRIDACEAE
SCIENTIFIC NAME:
Sisyrinchium atlanticum Bickn.
STATUS:
Missouri list - rare (relic)
POSSIBLE LOCATIONS:
Howell County
Mississippi County
Phelps County
Scott County
HABITAT:
Meadows, swales, marshes, low woods, and around sink-hole ponds
DESCRIPTION:
Flowering time:
Late April-June; perennial
Flower:
Blue-violet; spathe 1-1.5 cm long, pale green or purple-tinged; **peduncle thread-like.**
Leaves:
1-3 mm wide; pale green or **glaucous;** firm; narrow margined; usually 5 per clump, **not black when dried.**
Stem:
2-7 dm high; pale green or **glaucous; usually forking;** flattened.
Roots:
Not orange.
Fruit:
Head resembles a blackberry; **capsule 3-4.5 mm long.**

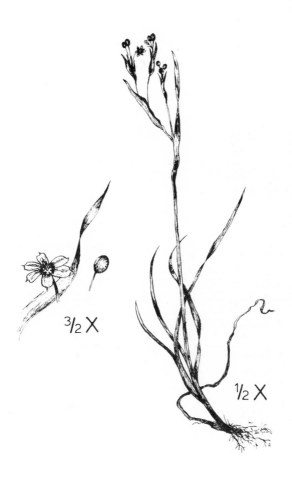

³/₂ X

½ X

SNAKE-MOUTH

FAMILY:

ORCHIDACEAE

SCIENTIFIC NAME:

Pogonia ophioglossoides (L.) Ker

STATUS:

Missouri list - undetermined

POSSIBLE LOCATIONS:

Reynolds County—calcareous swampy meadow bordering Spring Branch tributary to Middle Fork of Black River, along Highway 21, T.32N., R.1E., Sec. 15, 1.8 miles SW of bridge over Middle Fork, about 3 miles NE of Centerville

HABITAT:

Open bogs

DESCRIPTION:

Flowering time:

May-July; perennial

Flower:

Large; solitary or occasionally in pairs; subtended by a bract; petals pale to deep pink (rarely white); lip about as long as the sepals, pink, veined with red, bearded with yellow hairs; fragrant; 1-3 to a stem.

Leaves:

1-15 cm long; without hairs; basal leaves rarely seen; leaves on stem usually seen, **lanceolate or ovate;** ascending.

Stem:

2-4 dm high; slender.

Roots:

Fibrous.

WET LOWLAND
Pogonia ophioglossoides

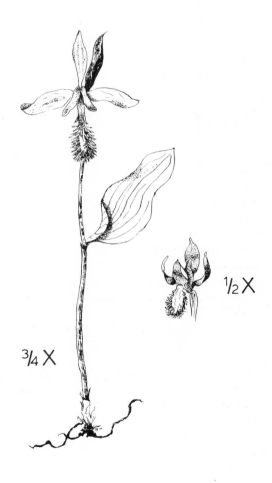

¾ X

½ X

133

PURPLE FRINGLESS ORCHID

FAMILY:
ORCHIDACEAE

SCIENTIFIC NAME:
Habenaria peramoena Gray

STATUS:
National list - threatened
Missouri list - rare

POSSIBLE LOCATIONS:
Bollinger County
Butler County
Carter County
Dunklin County
Iron County
Ripley County
St. Francois County
Stoddard County
Wayne County

HABITAT:
Low woods, meadows, bogs, damp or wet soil

DESCRIPTION:

Flowering time:
Late June-August; perennial

Flower:
Rose-purple to purple-violet; large inflorescence
6-18 cm long; flowers 5 to many per stem; lip
3-lobed, shallowly toothed (teeth 1 mm or less);
definite spur; lip not sac-like.

Leaves:
Lanceolate; 2-4 lower leaves are 10-20 cm; upper
leaves abruptly reduced; leaves present at
flowering time.

Stem:
3-10 dm high.

WET LOWLAND
Habenaria peramoena

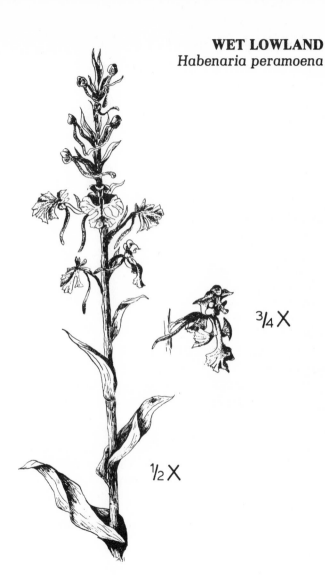

$^3/_4$ X

$^1/_2$ X

PRAIRIE WHITE FRINGED ORCHID

FAMILY:

ORCHIDACEAE

SCIENTIFIC NAME:

Habenaria leucophaea (Nutt.) Gray

STATUS:

National list - threatened
Missouri list - rare

POSSIBLE LOCATIONS:

Carter County
Clinton County
Greene County
Jackson County
Jasper County
Jefferson County
Lawrence County
Madison County
Newton County
Ralls County
St. Louis County
Vernon County

HABITAT:

Wet prairies, open swamps, bogs, marshes, and meadows

DESCRIPTION:

Flowering time:

June-August; perennial

Flower:

White or greenish-white; fragrant; **lateral petals toothed,** slightly longer than sepals; lip 3-lobed, long fringed; definite spur; lip not sac-like.

Leaves:

Lower leaves broadly linear, 10-20 cm, blunt; upper leaves much reduced; present at flowering time.

Stem:

4-10 dm high; stout.

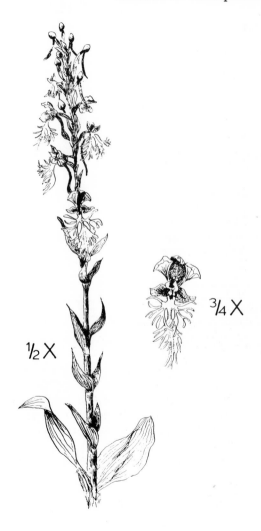

½ X

¾ X

137

PALE GREEN ORCHID

FAMILY:
ORCHIDACEAE

SCIENTIFIC NAME:
Habenaria flava var.*herbiola* (R. Br.) Ames and
Correll

STATUS:
National list - threatened

POSSIBLE LOCATIONS:
Butler County
Howell County
Iron County

HABITAT:
Swales, riverbottom prairies, low woods in valleys,
and bordering streams

DESCRIPTION:

Flowering time:
Late May-September; perennial

Flower:
Greenish to greenish-yellow and greenish-white;
inflorescence compact, 5 to many to a stem;
**lowest floral bracts often much exceeding
flowers;** definite spur; lip not sac-like; **lip margin
often irregular.**

Leaves:
2-5 large leaves on stem, up to 20 cm long and 5
cm wide; gradually decreasing in size towards
stem top; present at flowering time.

Stem:
1-7 dm high; stout.

Habenaria flava var. herbiola

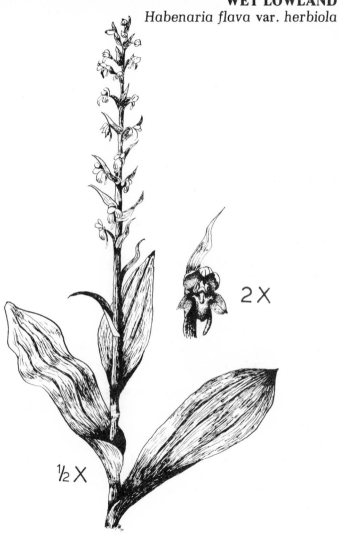

2X

½ X

PALE GREEN ORCHID

FAMILY:
ORCHIDACEAE

SCIENTIFIC NAME:
Habenaria flava (L.) R. Br. var. *flava*

STATUS:
National list - threatened

Missouri list - endangered

POSSIBLE LOCATIONS:
Livingston County
Shannon County
Wayne County

HABITAT:
Swales, riverbottom prairies, low woods in valleys bordering streams

DESCRIPTION:

Flowering time:
Late May-September; perennial

Flower:
Greenish to greenish-yellow and greenish-white; **inflorescence loosely flowered;** 5 to many flowers per stem; **most of bracts shorter than flower except for lowest bract which is slightly exceeding or equal;** definite spur; lip not sac-like; lip margin often irregular.

Leaves:
Usually 2 (less frequently 1 or 3); large, to 20 cm long and 5 cm wide; gradually decreasing in size towards stem top; present at flowering time.

Stem:
1-7 dm high; slender.

Habenaria flava var. flava

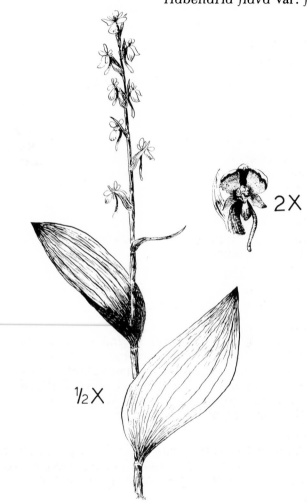

2X

½X

YELLOW FRINGED ORCHID

FAMILY:

ORCHIDACEAE

SCIENTIFIC NAME:

Habenaria ciliaris (L.) R. Br.

STATUS:

Missouri list - endangered

Edge of geographical range

POSSIBLE LOCATIONS:

Iron County

Ripley County—Pleasant Grove, margin of Cupola Pond T.25N., R.1W., Sec. 29, 1½ miles SE of Handy

Stoddard County

HABITAT:

Acid swamps and bogs; sandy wet ground along spring branches, margins of sink-hole ponds and moist pine woods

DESCRIPTION:

Flowering time:

July-October; perennial; blooms for a month.

Flower:

Orange or orange-yellow; arranged in a compact, many-flowered inflorescence 5-15 cm long; petals oblong, commonly hidden by the lateral sepals; **lip not 3-parted or 3-lobed** but is long-fringed; has a definite spur.

Leaves:

Several; up to 15 cm long and 4 cm wide; rapidly decreasing in size towards stem top; lower 1-3 leaves lanceolate; present at flowering time.

Stem:

3-9 dm tall; slender.

$^3/_2$ X

$^1/_2$ X

SHOWY LADY-SLIPPER

FAMILY:

ORCHIDACEAE

SCIENTIFIC NAME:

Cypripedium reginae Walt.

STATUS:

Missouri list - rare

Edge of geographical range

POSSIBLE LOCATIONS:

Douglas County

Howell County

Iron County

Ozark County—North Fork of White River, north of Double Spring (Rainbow Spring), 4 miles NE of Dormis and 4 miles SE of Dora

Shannon County

Texas County

HABITAT:

Swamps, bogs, wet woods, and damp areas of north-facing limestone bluffs

DESCRIPTION:

Flowering time:

May-June; perennial

Flower:

1-3 flowers to a stem; **sepals and lateral petals white, blunt at tip and shorter than the lip; lip rose or rose-purplish with white;** lip is a large, showy, inflated, balloon-like pouch which is 18-55 mm long.

Leaves:

1-2 dm long and half as wide; densely covered with hairs; leaves mainly on stem, not at base; strongly ribbed; present at time of flowering.

Stem:

4-10 m tall; stout; densely covered with hairs. The hairs have glands which contain a substance often irritating to persons handling the plant.

144

WET LOWLAND
Cypripedium reginae

½ X

½ X

CORKWOOD

FAMILY:
LEITNERIACEAE

SCIENTIFIC NAME:
Leitneria floridana Chapm.

STATUS:
Missouri list - endangered

POSSIBLE LOCATIONS:
Butler County
Dunklin County
Pemiscot County
Ripley County

HABITAT:
Swamps and wet thickets

DESCRIPTION:

Flowering time:
March-April

Flower:
Male and female flowers in separate catkins; male catkins many-flowered, 3 cm long; female few-flowered, 1.5 cm long.

Leaves:
7-15 cm long; oblong; leathery; dark olive to dull green; more or less crowded near the top of the new seasons growth; remain green until late autumn.

Stem:
Shrub or small tree; 7.5 m (25 ft.) but is often only 1 m (3¼ ft.) tall; slightly enlarged at the base; wood is lighter than cork.

½ X

½ X

1 X

SMARTWEED

FAMILY:
POLYGONACEAE

SCIENTIFIC NAME:
Polygonum densiflorum Meisn.

STATUS:
Missouri list - rare

POSSIBLE LOCATIONS:
Barton County
Carter County
Dunklin County
Scott County

HABITAT:
West swampy woods, thickets, and shallow water

DESCRIPTION:

Flowering time:
August-October; **perennial**

Flower:
White or whitish; in spikes, erect or slightly arching, 2-11 cm long; **peduncle with hairs lying parallel to the surface.**

Leaves:
0.7-3 dm long; lanceolate; pointed on both ends; without hairs, midrib prominent beneath.

Stem:
0.6-2 m high; without hairs; sheathing stipules surrounding stem lacking a fringe of bristles at the top.

Roots:
Forking rootstocks; **rhizomes**

2 X

½ X

POND BERRY

FAMILY:
LAURACEAE

SCIENTIFIC NAME:
Lindera melissaefolium (Walt.) Blume

STATUS:
National list - threatened

Missouri list - rare

POSSIBLE LOCATIONS:
Barry County—near Roaring River State Park
Ripley County—wooded depression, T.22N., R.4E,
Sec. 35, 4 miles south of Naylor

HABITAT:
Swamps and pond margins

DESCRIPTION:

Flowering time:
March-April

Flower:
Yellow; male and female separate; in umbel-like
clusters that appear before leaves.

Leaves:
Up to 1.5 dm long; **rounded or cordate at base;**
not lobed; **leaf blades drooping.**

Stem:
0.3-1.8 m high; shrub; with pubescent branches
and buds.

Fruit:
Scarlet drupe 10-11.5 mm long and 7-8 mm
wide; **fruit stalks remain until next year's flowering.**

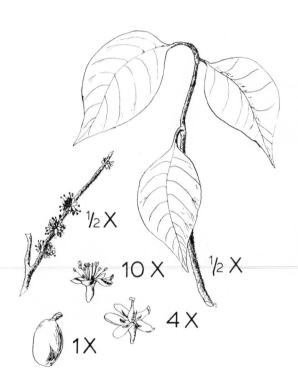

½ X

10 X   ½ X

4 X

1X

STONECROP

FAMILY:
CRASSULACEAE

SCIENTIFIC NAME:
Sedum ternatum Michx.

STATUS:
Uncommon but not listed

POSSIBLE LOCATIONS:
Barry County
Christian County
Marion County

HABITAT:
Damp rocks, mossy banks, cliffs, and woods

DESCRIPTION:

Flowering time:
April-June; perennial

Flower:
1 cm wide; **white;** sessile.

Leaves:
1-3 cm long; green, entire; ones on sterile shoots and the lower ones of the fertile shoots in whorls of 3; **narrowed at base and broadly rounded at summit;** upper leaves of fertile stem opposite or alternate, linear.

Stem:
Less than 2 dm tall; **creeping stems sending up a single flowering stem** and several short leafy sterile stems.

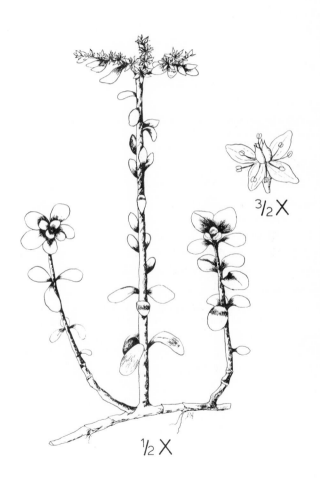

$^3/_2$ X

$^1/_2$ X

QUEEN OF THE PRAIRIE

FAMILY:

ROSACEAE

SCIENTIFIC NAME:

Filipendula rubra (Hill) Robins

STATUS:

Missouri list - endangered (relic)

POSSIBLE LOCATIONS:

Reynolds County—along west fork of Black River, T.33N., R.3W., Sec. 23 and NE Sec. 26, 3-3½ miles NW of Greely

HABITAT:

Low woods, wet prairies or meadows

DESCRIPTION:

Flowering time:

June-August; perennial

Flower:

7-10 mm wide; **pink; calyx not bristly.**

Leaves:

Terminal leaflet large; 7-9 parted, lobes toothed; 2-5 pairs of lateral leaflets shallowly to deeply 3-5 lobed.

Stem:

6-25 dm tall; without hairs.

Fruit:

Achenes erect; without hairs; oblong.

WET LOWLAND
Filipendula rubra

½ X

2 X

MUSCADINE GRAPE

FAMILY:

VITACEAE

SCIENTIFIC NAME:

Vitis rotundifolia Michx.

STATUS:

Missouri list - rare

POSSIBLE LOCATIONS:

Dunklin County

Madison County

Pemiscot County

HABITAT:

Low wet woods, borders of swamps, and bayous

DESCRIPTION:

Flowering time:

May-June

Fruiting time:

September-October

Flower:

Petals fall before flower opens; in panicles 2-5 cm long; densely flowered.

Leaves:

6-12 cm wide; cordate-ovate; glossy on both sides; with teeth or lobes.

Stem:

Vine; glabrous; sends out aerial drooping roots from the branches especially in flooded bottomlands; **pith continuous through the nodes; tendrils not forked.**

Bark:

Not shedding.

Fruit:

A thick, tough skin, purple-black to bronze berry without a bloom; 12-25 mm in diameter.

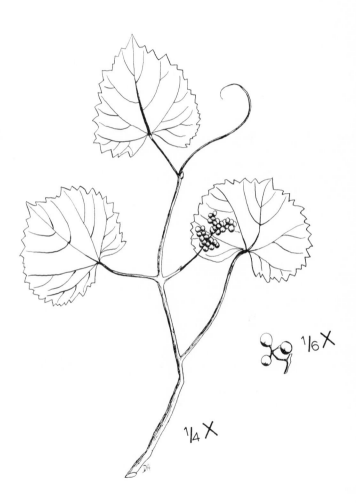

¹/₁₆ X

¹/₄ X

MARSH ST. JOHN'S WORT

FAMILY:
HYPERICACEAE

SCIENTIFIC NAME:
Hypericum tubulosum Walt.

STATUS:
Missouri list - rare

POSSIBLE LOCATIONS:
Butler County
Dunklin County
Stoddard County
Wayne County

HABITAT:
Low wet woods, bayous, and bald cypress swamps

DESCRIPTION:

Flowering time:
August-September; perennial

Flower:
Pink or salmon; stamens 9.

Leaves:
4-15 cm long; **rounded to heart-shape at base;** pale green; membranaceous; **lower surface without dark dots or translucent round glands.**

Stem:
6-10 dm high, branched above.

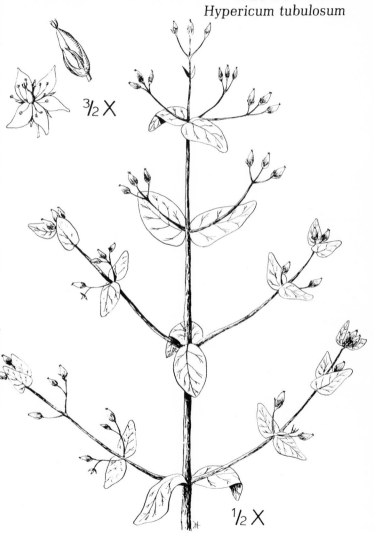

3/2 X

1/2 X

SMOOTH WHITE VIOLET

FAMILY:
VIOLACEAE

SCIENTIFIC NAME:
Viola pallens (Banks) Brainerd

STATUS:
Missouri list - rare (relic)

POSSIBLE LOCATIONS:
Southeastern Ozarks
Ste. Genevieve County—moist sandstone ledge
near spring along River aux Vases at base of
bluff about 5 miles NE of Pickle
—also known from along
Pickle Creek, Terre Bleue Creek, Hickory
Creek, and River aux Vases

HABITAT:
Can be found in shallow water, springy land,
thickets, slopes, and along cold streams

DESCRIPTION:
Flowering time:
April-May

Flower:
White; the 3 lower petals with brown-purple
veins near the base; **the 2 lateral with or without
a small beard of hairs.**

Leaves:
Leaf blade and leaf stalk without hairs; leaf
broadly cordate-ovate, round, or very blunt-
tipped.

Stem:
Stemless; leaves and flower rise near the surface
of the ground; **sends out thread-like runners
from the base.**

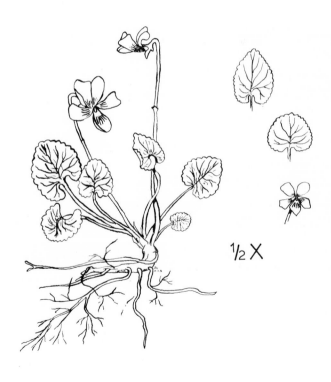

½ X

FALSE LOOSESTRIFE

FAMILY:
ONAGRACEAE

SCIENTIFIC NAME:
Ludwigia microcarpa Michx.

STATUS:
Missouri list - undetermined

POSSIBLE LOCATIONS:
Oregon County—swampy meadow bordering "Hatcher's Spring" along Spring Branch below Greer Spring, 1 mile north of Greer

HABITAT:
Ditches, wet thickets, swampy meadows

DESCRIPTION:

Flowering time:
July-October; perennial

Flower:
Without petals; greenish; sessile in the leaf axils.

Leaves:
0.5-2.5 cm long; obovate; tapering to petioles.

Stem:
1-5 dm high; slender; depressed or loosely ascending; stems angled.

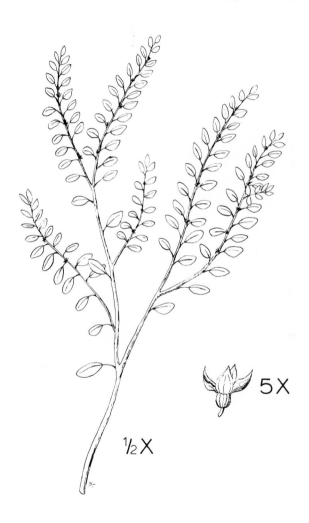

½X

5X

MOCK BISHOP'S WEED

FAMILY:
UMBELLIFERAE

SCIENTIFIC NAME:
Ptilimnium capillaceum (Michx.) Raf.

STATUS:
Missouri list - undetermined

POSSIBLE LOCATIONS:
Iron County

HABITAT:
Wet ground

DESCRIPTION:

Flowering time:
June-August; annual

Flower:
White; 5-15 rays of flowers per umbel; calyx teeth broadly triangular; **bracts at base of main rays 3-cleft.**

Leaves:
4-10 cm long; pinnately dissected into hair-like segments, 3 divisions at a node.

Stem:
2-8 dm; erect; slender; freely branched.

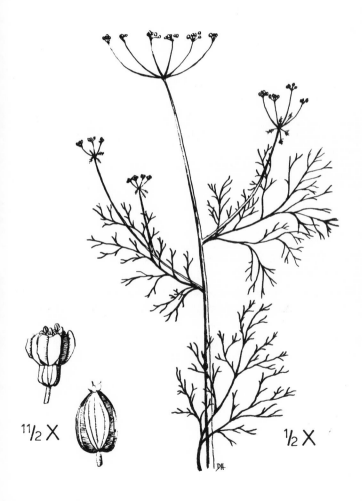

$1\!1/_2\,\mathsf{X}$

$1/_2\,\mathsf{X}$

DH

WATER PENNYWORT

FAMILY:
UMBELLIFERAE

SCIENTIFIC NAME:
Hydrocotyle verticillata Thunb.

STATUS:
Missouri list - undetermined

POSSIBLE LOCATIONS:
Ozark County—along North Fork of White River, north of Rainbow Spring, 4 miles SE of Dora

HABITAT:
Swamps, low grounds, and moist banks

DESCRIPTION:

Flowering time:
May-August; perennial

Flower:
Whitish; 1-12 umbels of 2-20 sessile flowers.

Leaves:
Up to 6 cm in diameter; **round; leaf stalk joining the leaf blade near the middle;** leaf with 8-14 shallow lobes.

Stem:
Creeping; without hairs.

WET LOWLAND
Hydrocotyle verticillata

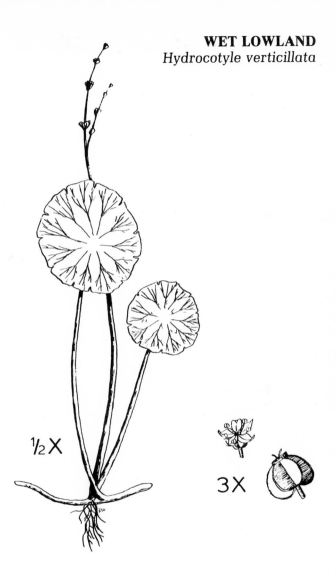

½X

3X

167

BUCKBEAN or BOGBEAN

FAMILY:

GENTIANACEAE

SCIENTIFIC NAME:

Menyanthes trifoliata L. var. *minor* Raf.

STATUS:

Missouri list - endangered (relic)

POSSIBLE LOCATIONS:

Reynolds County—along north prong of Bee Fork, 5 miles east of Bunker, T.32N., R.2W., Sec. 23

HABITAT:

Bogs and marshes

DESCRIPTION:

Flowering time:

April-May; perennial

Flower:

White or purple-tinged at tips; beard most abundant on lower half of lobes; 10-20 flowers on scape.

Leaves:

3-6 cm long; **3 oval or oblong sessile leaflets;** petioles of leaves sheathed at the base.

Stem:

Creeping thick rootstock; white or slightly reddish scape with flowers is 1-3 dm high.

WET LOWLAND
Menyanthes trifoliata var. minor

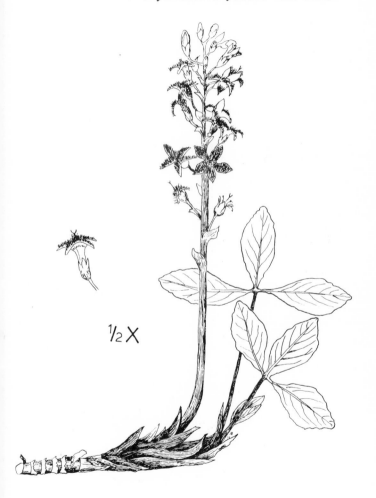

½ X

WILD SWEET WILLIAM

FAMILY:

POLEMONIACEAE

SCIENTIFIC NAME:

Phlox maculata L. var. *pyramidalis* (Smith)
Wherry

STATUS:

Missouri list - rare

Edge of geographical range

POSSIBLE LOCATIONS:

Carter County
Dent County
Iron County
Reynolds County
Ste. Genevieve County

HABITAT:

Meadows, bottomlands, and streambank

DESCRIPTION:

Flowering time:

Late May-October; perennial

Flower:

Deep rose-red to reddish-purple; inflorescence
terminal; **many cymes.**

Leaves:

5-12 cm long; numerous; lanceolate-linear or
narrowly oblong.

Stem:

3-8 dm erect; **usually red-spotted.**

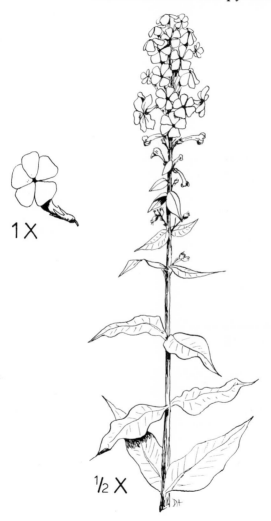

1 X

½ X

OVATE-LEAVED NAMA

FAMILY:

HYDROPHYLLACEAE

SCIENTIFIC NAME:

Hydrolea ovata Nutt.

STATUS:

Missouri list - endangered

POSSIBLE LOCATIONS:

Butler County

Dunklin County

Howell County—margin of sink-hole pond of Tingle Lake, T.23N., R.8W., south part of Sec. 32, 8 miles south of West Plains

—small upland pond along south side of Highway 80, 7½ miles SW of West Plains

HABITAT:

Swamps, sloughs, and margins of ponds

DESCRIPTION:

Flowering time:

June-September

Flower:

Blue; broadly bell-shaped; **in terminal** leafy panicles; calyx hairy.

Leaves:

4-10 cm long; **ovate;** spines usually present in the axils of the leaves.

Stem:

3-8 dm; creeping at base; **upper half densely hairy.**

WET LOWLAND
Hydrolea ovata

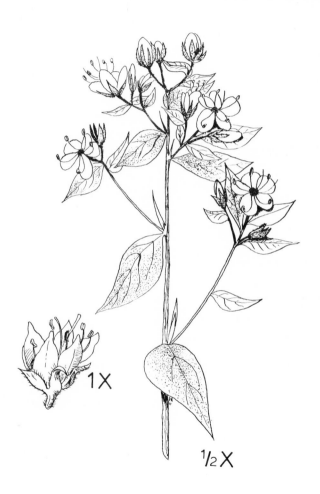

1X

½X

HEARTLEAF PLANTAIN

FAMILY:
PLANTAGINACEAE
SCIENTIFIC NAME:
Plantago cordata Lam.
STATUS:
National list - threatened
POSSIBLE LOCATIONS:

Adair County
Boone County
Butler County
Carter County
Crawford County
Dent County
Franklin County
Howard County
Iron County
Jefferson County
Maries County

Montgomery County
Oregon County
Osage County
Ripley County
St. Louis County
Ste. Genevieve County
Shannon County
Texas County
Warren County
Washington County

HABITAT:
Marshes, in and along streams and in swampy
woods
DESCRIPTION:
Flowering time:
May-July; perennial
Flower:
Whitish or pale; small; in a loosely flowered
slender spike up to 4.5 dm long; **flowering stems
hollow.**
Leaves:
1-3 dm long; dark green; fleshy; **heart shaped** or
broadly ovate; entire or dentate; on a long stalk;
**main side nerves of leaves start from the midrib
within the blade of the leaf.**
Stem:
Tall; without hairs; flowering stem hollow.
Roots:
Fleshy.

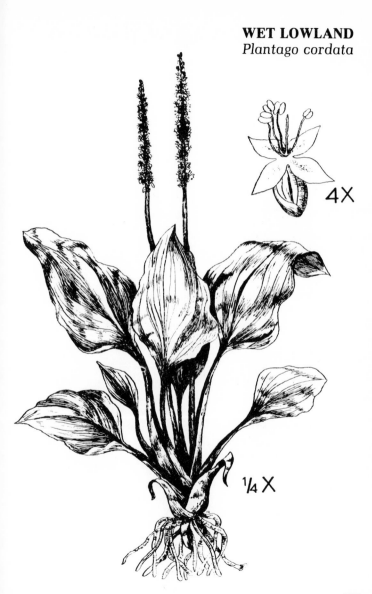

WET LOWLAND
Plantago cordata

4X

¼X

ARROW-WOOD

FAMILY:

CAPRIFOLIACEAE

SCIENTIFIC NAME:

Viburnum recognitum Fern.

STATUS:

Missouri list-endangered

Edge of geographical range

POSSIBLE LOCATIONS:

Oregon County—margin of dry gravel bar of creek along Little Hurricane Creek, vicinity of "Blue Hole," T.24N., R.3W., Sec. 5, 2½-3 miles east of Greer

HABITAT:

Damp thickets and gravel bars of small streams

DESCRIPTION:

Flowering time:

May-June

Flower:

White (rarely pink); in cymes; without hairs or essentially without hairs.

Leaves:

3-9 cm long and 2-8 cm broad; **orbicular to narrowly ovate or oblong;** veins prominent beneath; coarse acute teeth; petioles up to 3 cm long and without hairs; leaves without hairs on upper surface; **stipules usually absent.**

Stem:

1-3 m high; shrub; **branches glabrous.**

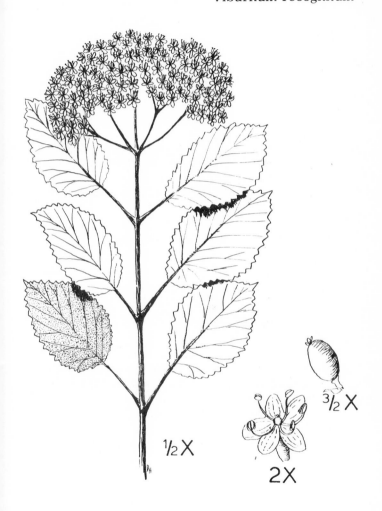

1/2 X

2X

3/2 X

WILD ASTER

FAMILY:
COMPOSITAE

SCIENTIFIC NAME:
Aster dumosus var. *dodgei* Fern.

STATUS:
Missouri list - rare

POSSIBLE LOCATIONS:
Howell County—swampy remnant in field, T.23N., R.8W., Sec. 23, 6½ miles SE of West Plains

HABITAT:
Marshy ground

DESCRIPTION:

Flowering time:
August-November; perennial

Flower:
Rays 18-24, 5-9 mm long, pale-lavender or bluish (rarely white); disk-flowers 15-30, pale yellow or brown, 3-4 mm long; heads numerous, **solitary at the ends of the branches.**

Leaves:
3-11 cm long and 3-8 mm wide; linear to lanceolate-linear; sessile; entire or nearly so; **harshly scabrous on both sides.**

Stem:
Up to 9 dm high; slender; **with dense, ashy, short, stiff hairs.**

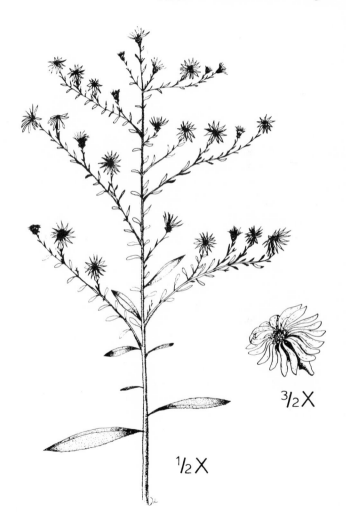

½ X

³/₂ X

MARSH FLEABANE

FAMILY:
COMPOSITAE

SCIENTIFIC NAME:
Pluchea foetida (L.) D.C.

STATUS:
Missouri list - endangered

POSSIBLE LOCATIONS:
Butler County

HABITAT:
Wet sand, ditches, swamps, and wet meadows

DESCRIPTION:

Flowering time:
July-September; perennial

Flower:
Creamy; heads clustered in a corymb.

Leaves:
4-10 cm long and 1-4 cm wide; **sessile and clasping;** oblong to lanceolate.

Stem:
5-9 dm high; glandular.

$^{3}/_{2}$ X

$^{1}/_{2}$ X

OTHER PLANTS SOMETIMES FOUND IN SWAMPS, SWALES, BOGS AND WET WOODS

AQUATIC SPECIES

PONDWEED

FAMILY:
NAJADACEAE

SCIENTIFIC NAME:
Potamogeton epihydrus Raf. var. *nuttallii* (C. & S.) Fern

STATUS:
Missouri list - rare (relic)

POSSIBLE LOCATIONS:
Reynolds County—Lily Pond, 7 miles SE of Centerville

HABITAT:
Ponds, slow streams, lakes, and sinkholes

DESCRIPTION:

Flowering time:
July-September

Flower:
Mature spike 1.8-4 cm long; spikes numerous, dense; peduncles from axils of floating leaves.

Leaves:
Submerged leaves 2-8 mm broad, 3-7 nerved; floating leaves sessile, narrowly oblong or oblong-lanceolate, rounded at tip, 7-33 nerved; floating leaves mostly opposite, tapering into flattened stalks; numerous.

Stem:
Creeping; **stem flattened;** simple or slightly branched.

Potamogeton epihydrus var. nuttallii

½ X

5 X

PONDWEED

FAMILY:
NAJADACEAE

SCIENTIFIC NAME:
Potamogeton pusillus L.

STATUS:
Missouri list - rare

POSSIBLE LOCATIONS:
Pettis County
Ripley County

HABITAT:
Ponds, lakes, slow-water of streams

DESCRIPTION:

Flowering time:
June-October

Flower:
Hairlike peduncles **1-5 cm long** grow from the upper axils; 1-3 whorls of flowers in a spike.

Leaves:
1-7 cm long; all submerged; narrowly linear; 3-nerved, lateral nerves often hard to see; **2 minute glands at base;** stipules not united with the base of the leaf.

Stem:
Slender; **numerous branches.**

AQUATIC
Potamogeton pusillus

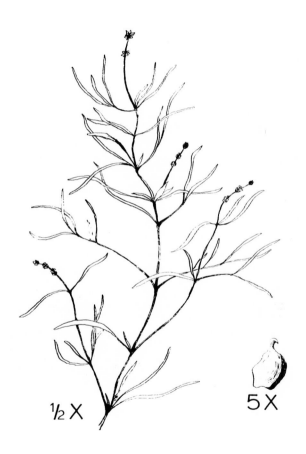

½ X

5 X

NAIAD

FAMILY:
NAJADACEAE

SCIENTIFIC NAME:
Najas gracillima (A. Br.) Magnus

STATUS:
Missouri list - rare

POSSIBLE LOCATIONS:
Shannon County
Texas County—3½ miles south of Licking

HABITAT:
Ponds and upland sinkholes

DESCRIPTION:

Flowering time:
July-September

Flower:
Both male and female flowers borne in the axils of branchlets and in sheaths of leaf-bases.

Leaves:
1.5-3.5 cm long; well scattered; straight, linear; somewhat divergent from the non-green, thin and chaffy sheathing base; lower third of leaf entire, upper two-thirds with 6-20 remote usually 3-celled little horns; **the sheath with conspicuous rounded to truncate 4-7 toothed lobes.**

Stem:
Very slender and delicate.

8X   5/2X   1X

9X

3X

BUR-HEAD

FAMILY:
ALISMACEAE

SCIENTIFIC NAME:
Echinodorus tenellus (Mart.) Buch. var. *parvulus* (Englem.) Fassett

STATUS:
Missouri list - rare

POSSIBLE LOCATIONS:
Howell County—Adobesse Pond, T.22N., R.7W., SE Sec. 36, 9 miles SE of West Plains
St. Louis County

HABITAT:
Shallow water, upland sinkhole ponds

DESCRIPTION:

Flower:

Flowering time:
August-September; short-lived perennial

Flower:
Flower 6 mm broad; white or pink; 2-8 flowers in an umbel; **stamens 6 or 9.**

Leaves:
1-3 cm long; basal; **mostly narrow;** linear-lanceolate, **tapering at each end.**

Stem:
1.5-10 cm long; shoots often creeping.

Fruit:
Without beaks.

Echinodorus tenellus var. parvulus

⁵/₂X

³/₂X

191

ARROW ARUM

FAMILY:

ARACEAE

SCIENTIFIC NAME:

Peltandra virginica (L.) Schott and Endl. f. *virginica*

STATUS:

Missouri list - rare

POSSIBLE LOCATIONS:

Cape Girardeau County

Jefferson County

St. Charles County

St. Louis County

Wayne County

HABITAT:

Wet, mucky ground bordering sloughs, ponds, slow streams, and oxbow lakes of river bottoms.

DESCRIPTION:

Flowering time:

April-June

Flower:

1-2 dm tall; spathe is green with a pale wavy margin and tightly convolute throughout; spadix is white to orange, nearly as long as spathe, and is a mass of tiny flowers throughout, not just at the base.

Leaves:

Blades arrow-head shaped; **lobes at base of leaf-blade 3-7.5 cm broad; main upper part of leaf-blade 8-18 cm broad;** simple; leaves fragrant.

Stem:

2-4 dm high.

Roots:

Very large; perpendicular, not fragrant.

Fruit:

Berries are green to brownish; head surrounded at the base by the spathe with a beaklike summit.

AQUATIC
Peltandra virginica

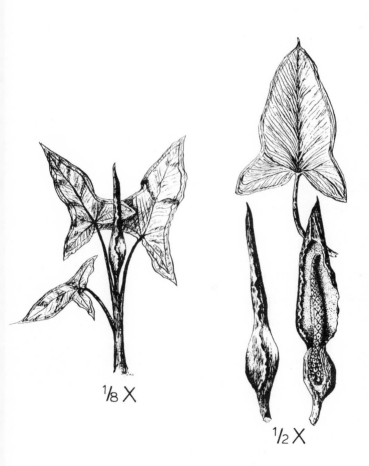

1/8 X

1/2 X

STAR DUCKWEED

FAMILY:
LEMNACEAE

SCIENTIFIC NAME:
Lemna trisulca L.

STATUS:
Missouri list - rare

POSSIBLE LOCATIONS:
Jackson County
Mercer County
Oregon County
Ripley County
Shannon County

HABITAT:
Cold, fresh water springs and ponds

DESCRIPTION:

Plant:
Usually submerged

Roots:
One to a plant; occasionally absent.

Leaves:
4-10 mm long; oblong to oblong-lanceolate; **narrowing at base into a slender stalk; usually several offshoots remain connected and this forms tangled masses in the water** which have a dark blue-green color; obscurely 3-nerved.

NOTE:
A microscope may be needed to distinquish among **Lemna** species.

AQUATIC
Lemna trisulca

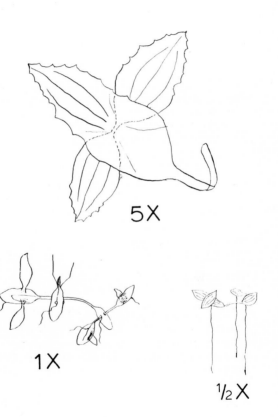

5X

1X

½X

195

LEAST DUCKWEED

FAMILY:
LEMNACEAE

SCIENTIFIC NAME:
Lemna minima Philippi

STATUS:
Missouri list - rare

POSSIBLE LOCATIONS:
Howell County—between Moody and South Fork, Sec. 7, 2 miles south of South Fork
Oregon County—Tupelo Gum Pond, Irish Wilderness, Sec. 4

HABITAT:
Natural sinkhole ponds

DESCRIPTION:

Plant:
Usually floating on surface.

Roots:
One to a plant.

Leaves:
1.5-3 mm long and 1-2 mm wide; green; are oblong to elliptic, rounded at the base; convex on upper side, **flat beneath; has 1 weak nerve.**

NOTE:
A microscope may be needed to distinguish among **Lemna** species.

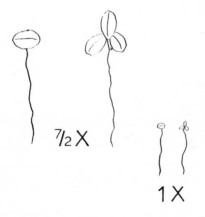

7/2 X

1 X

WATER-MEAL

FAMILY:
LEMNACEAE

SCIENTIFIC NAME:
Wolffia punctata Griseb.

STATUS:
Missouri list - rare

POSSIBLE LOCATIONS:
Phelps County—Yancy Mills Spring

HABITAT:
On surface of quiet water, cool springs

DESCRIPTION:

Plant:
Smallest flowering plant known; floats on surface.

Roots:
None present

Leaves:
1.5 mm long at most; oblong; **upper suface is nearly flat except for one tiny bump raised at one end (not center);** deep green with many stomata above and pale below, numerous brown dots all over.

NOTE:
A microscope may be needed to distinguish among **Wolffia** species.

18 X

³/₂ X

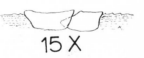

15 X

WATERWORT

FAMILY:
ELATINACEAE

SCIENTIFIC NAME:
Elatine triandra Schkuhr var. *americana* (Pursh.)
Fassett

STATUS:
Missouri list - endangered

POSSIBLE LOCATIONS:
Jackson County
Laclede County

HABITAT:
Upland sinkhole ponds and muddy swales

DESCRIPTION:

Flowering time:
June-October

Flower:
Small; pink; 3 petals; flowers sessile and solitary
in the leaf-axils.

Leaves:
3-8 (rarely to 10) mm long; obovate; **entire;
rounded at summit; glabrous.**

Stem:
Creeping or floating in small mats; branches 1-5
cm long; **glabrous.**

AQUATIC
Elatine triandra var. americana

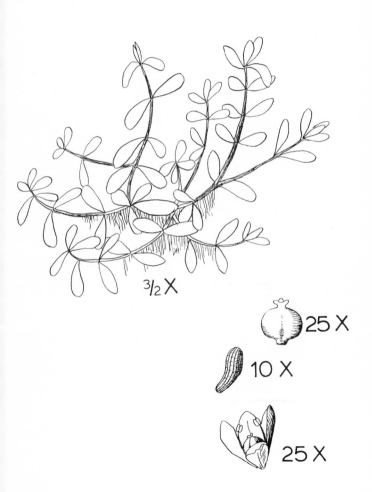

³/₂ X

25 X

10 X

25 X

SWAMP LOOSESTRIFE or WATER WILLOW

FAMILY:
LYTHRACEAE
SCIENTIFIC NAME:
Decodon verticillatus (L.) Ell.
STATUS:
Missouri list - endangered
POSSIBLE LOCATIONS:
Boone County—Ashland Wildlife Preserve
Reynolds County—Bowles Pond, in upland tributary to Harrison Valley, T.31N., R.1E., Sec. 23, 2½ miles NW of Redford
—Lily Pond, T.31N., R.1E., NW ¼, Sec. 23, south of Vinson Hole, 2-¾ miles NW of Centerville

HABITAT:
Upland sinkhole ponds

DESCRIPTION:
Flowering time:
July-September; perennial

Flower:
10 15 mm long; pink-purple; in dense clusters in the upper axils.

Leaves:
5-15 cm long and 1-3 cm wide; opposite or in whorls of 3 or 4; lanceolate, **narrowed at base;** entire; nearly sessile.

Stem:
Somewhat woody below with slender arched stems 1-3 m long, submerged part of stem has spongy thickened bark.

Roots:
Spreads by rooting at tips of its arching branches.

AQUATIC
Decodon verticillatus

½ X

2X

HEDGE HYSSOP

FAMILY:
SCROPHULARIACEAE

SCIENTIFIC NAME:
Gratiola viscidula Pennell

STATUS:
Missouri list - endangered (relic)

POSSIBLE LOCATIONS:
Shannon County—Gilmore Pond (Grassy Pond), T.27N., R.6W., Sec. 34 between Jack's Fork of Current River and Flat Rock Hollow, 6½ miles NW of Monteer

HABITAT:
Upland sinkhole ponds

DESCRIPTION:

Flowering time:
June-September; **perennial**

Flower:
White or tinged with purple, marked with purple lines internally.

Leaves:
1-2.5 cm long; **main leaves of stem broadest at or near the rounded base,** lanceolate to ovate; several small, sharp teeth; 3-5 nerved.

Stem:
1-6.5 dm long; bases partly submerged; grows in dense masses; flowering stem glandular.

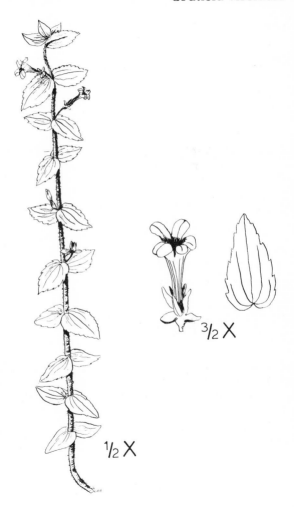

3/2 X

1/2 X

MONKEY FLOWER

FAMILY:

SCROPHULARIACEAE

SCIENTIFIC NAME:

Mimulus glabratus HBK. var. *fremontii* (Benth.) Grant

STATUS:

Missouri list - rare

Edge of geographical range

POSSIBLE LOCATIONS:

Barry County
Greene County
Lawrence County
Ste. Genevieve County

HABITAT:

Springs, brooks, and wet ledges along bluffs

DESCRIPTION:

Flowering time:

May-October; perennial

Flower:

8-12 mm long; yellow, sometimes with reddish-brown dots; arising at the sides of the stem at the base of the leaves.

Leaves:

1-4 cm long; **suborbicular,** oval or cordate to reniform; margin entire, or nearly denticulate, or undulate.

Stem:

Spreading or creeping along the ground; roots at nodes.

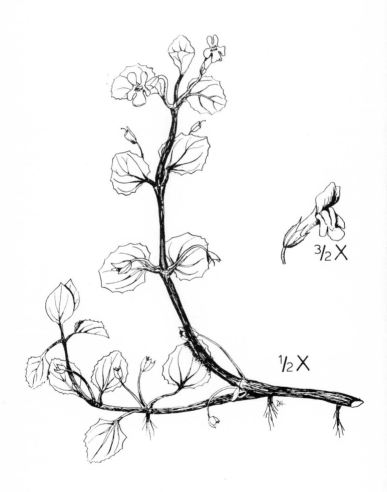

3/2 X

1/2 X

CLUSTERED BLUETS

FAMILY:
RUBIACEAE

SCIENTIFIC NAME:
Oldenlandia boscii (D.C.) Chapm.

STATUS:
Missouri list - rare

POSSIBLE LOCATIONS:
Ripley County—dried out depression, T.22N., R.4E., Sec. 36, 4 miles south of Naylor

HABITAT:
Sandy borders of streams and ponds, swampy ground

DESCRIPTION:

Flowering time:
July-October; perennial

Flower:
White; flowers in small axillary and terminal glomerules.

Leaves:
1-3 cm long and 1-2.5 mm wide; **linear,** narrowed at base; **glabrous.**

Stem:
1-3 dm high; without hairs; numerous diffusely branched stems; **glabrous.**

Fruit:
Smooth or slightly rough.

7/2 X

15/2 X

1/2 X

OTHER PLANTS SOMETIMES FOUND IN
SINKHOLES, STREAMS AND PONDS

PRAIRIE SPECIES

WHITE CAMAS

FAMILY:

LILIACEAE

SCIENTIFIC NAME:

Zigadenus elegans Pursh.

STATUS:

Missouri list - rare (relic)

POSSIBLE LOCATIONS:

Douglas County—along Indian Creek, Holy Cliff and vicinity T.26-27N., R.11W., Sec. 4, and 33, 3½ miles NE of Topaz

Pulaski County—along the Gasconade River by Peterson Cave, Sec. 8, 5 miles NW of Waynesville

Shannon County—Jam-up Bluff

HABITAT:

Prairies, meadows, and moist crevices of limestone bluffs

DESCRIPTION:

Flowering time:

June-August; perennial

Flower:

8-12 mm long; pale white with or without a small darkened spot outside at base; **gland at base of petals is 2-lobed;** inflorescence a slender raceme, upper and middle bracts with thin and chaffy margins.

Leaves:

2-4 dm long and up to 12 mm wide; linear; few; main leaves from base of plant.

Stem:

2.5-9 dm high.

Roots:

A bulb; outer coat fibrous (not papery) and very glaucous.

NOTE:

Poisonous

1X

3/8 X

SUNDROPS

FAMILY:
ONAGRACEAE

SCIENTIFIC NAME:
Oenothera perennis L.

STATUS:
Missouri list - undetermined

Edge of geographical range

POSSIBLE LOCATIONS:
Dent County—T.32N., R.4W., Sec. 30,
¾ mile south of Turtle P.O.

HABITAT:
Moist or dry soil, fields, meadows, and open woods

DESCRIPTION:

Flowering time:
June-August; perennial

Flower:
Yellow; **inflorescence drooping;** flowers become erect and open one at a time.

Leaves:
3-6 cm long; oblanceolate to elliptic, narrowed at base; bracteal leaves linear, entire, or with a few fine teeth.

Stem:
2-6 dm tall; erect; 1-several stems.

PRAIRIE
Oenothera perennis

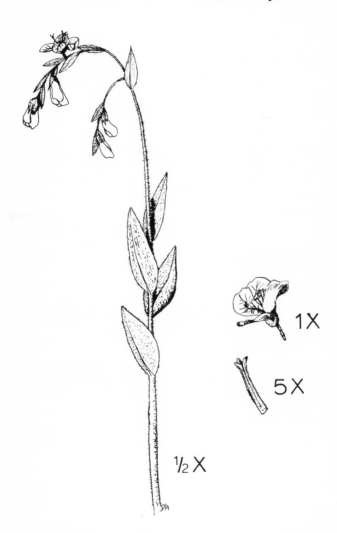

1X

5X

½X

MARSH BELLFLOWER

FAMILY:
CAMPANULACEAE

SCIENTIFIC NAME:
Campanula aparinoides L.

STATUS:
Missouri list - endangered (relic)

POSSIBLE LOCATIONS:
Newton County
Shannon County—swamps, meadow along Big
Creek, T.31N., R.3W., NW ¼, Sec. 8, 2¼
miles south of Melton, 4¼ miles SE of Bunker.

HABITAT:
Meadows and swales

DESCRIPTION:

Flowering time:
June-August; perennial

Flower:
5-8 mm long; **whitish,** or pale blue; funnelform;
solitary on long slender pedicels.

Leaves:
8 cm long and 8 mm wide; lanceolate or linear-
lanceolate; sessile; **often roughed on the
margins and midvein beneath.**

Stem:
3-10 dm; weak, slender, usually reclining on
other plants; somewhat 3-angled; rough with
short bristles.

PRAIRIE
Campanula aparinoides

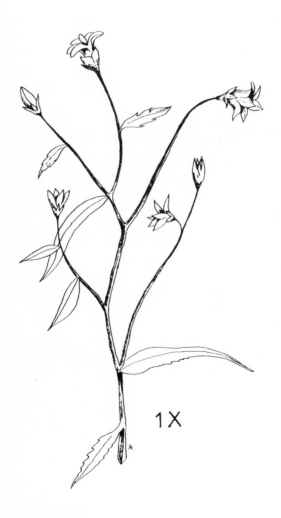

1X

BUTTON SNAKEROOT

FAMILY:
COMPOSITAE

SCIENTIFIC NAME:
Liatris spicata (L.) Willd.

STATUS:
Uncommon but not listed

Edge of geographical range

POSSIBLE LOCATIONS:
Oregon County—prairie opening along railroad, 3 miles north of Koshkonong
—gravelly open ground near Bardley

HABITAT:
Moist open places, meadows, borders of marshes, savannas, and damp slopes

DESCRIPTION:

Flowering time:
July-August; perennial

Flower:
Rose-purple; flowers 10-18; in a dense spike 0.6-7 dm long; without hairs within; **bracts rounded.**

Leaves:
1-4 dm long and 0.5-2 mm broad, lower ones widest; numerous; linear; **glabrous.**

Stem:
0.3-1.8 m high; stiff; **glabrous.**

PRAIRIE
Liatris spicata

½ X

½ X

WILD ASTER

FAMILY:
COMPOSITAE

SCIENTIFIC NAME:
Aster dumosus var. *strictior* T. and G.

STATUS:
Missouri list - rare

POSSIBLE LOCATIONS:
Butler County
Howell County—meadow along north side of
Highway 80, 4.9 miles SW of West Plains

HABITAT:
Dry to wet open ground

DESCRIPTION:

Flowering time:
August-November; perennial

Flower:
Rays 13-20, 5-9 mm long, pale lavender or bluish
(rarely white); disk-flowers 15-30, 3-4 mm long,
pale yellow or brown; heads solitary at the **tips
of numerous branchlets; have many small bract-
like leaves.**

Leaves:
3-11 cm long and 3-8 mm wide; linear to lance-
linear; sessile; entire or nearly so; **smooth.**

Stem:
Slender; up to 9 dm high; **without hairs or spar-
ingly with hairs;** branches forking.

½ X

1 X

NARROW-LEAVED MARSHALLIA

FAMILY:
COMPOSITAE

SCIENTIFIC NAME:
Marshallia caespitosa var. *signata* Beadle and Boynt

STATUS:
Uncommon but not listed

Edge of geographical range

POSSIBLE LOCATIONS:
Ozark County

HABITAT:
Prairies, glades, and openings

DESCRIPTION:

Flowering time:
April-June; perennial

Flower:
White, sometimes pink; **2-12 (or more) heads of flowers** on stem; flowers all tubular.

Leaves:
Basal and **located at various other levels; part of stem with leaves is as long or longer (rarely shorter) than the part without leaves.**

Stem:
1.5-4 dm high.

Marshallia caespitosa var. signata

½ X

1 X

⅜ X

OTHER PLANTS SOMETIMES FOUND IN PRAIRIES, FIELDS OR MEADOWS

ILLUSTRATED GLOSSARY

Achene--------------- a dry indehiscent one-seeded fruit.

Acuminate ---------- tapering to a slender point.

Acute---------------- ending in a point, sides essentially straight.

Alternate ------------ placed singly at different heights on the stem (fig. 5).

Ament---------------- A dense spike bearing many small flowers; same as catkin.

Annual--------------- living one year.

Ascending----------- growing upward.

Awn------------------ a slender, terminal bristle (fig. 10).

Axil ------------------ the position between a lateral organ (leaf branch or pedicel) and the stem (fig. 9).

Basal----------------- located at the base of a plant.

Biennial-------------- living two years only and flowering the second year.

Blade ---------------- the expanded, usually flat portion of a leaf (fig. 9).

Bloom---------------- the whitish, powdery, and glaucous covering of a surface.

Bract----------------- a specialized leaf from the axil of which a flower or inflorescence arises (fig. 2).

Calyx ---------------- the sepals together, often green (fig. 1).

Catkin---------------- a dense spike bearing many small flowers; same as ament.

Cauline-------------- situated on the stem.

Chaffy--------------- a small, thin, dry, and membranous scale or bract.

Compound --------- composed of two or more separate leaflets (fig. 7).

Convolute----------- rolled together longitudinally.

Cordate ------------- heart-shaped with the point at the apex.

Corolla ------------- the petals together, often colored (fig. 1).

Corymb ------------- a short and broad, more or less flat-topped flower cluster with the outer flowers opening first (fig. 13).

Culm --------------- stem of grasses and sedges; usually hollow in grasses except at the swollen nodes.

Cyme --------------- a broad, more or less flat-topped flower cluster with the central flowers opening first (fig. 14).

Cymose ------------- cyme-like or bearing cymes.

Deciduous ---------- not persistent, not evergreen.

Denticulate -------- minutely toothed.

Disk-flower -------- in *Compositae,* the tubular flowers of the head as distinguished from the ray flowers (fig. 15).

Drupe -------------- a fleshy one-seeded indehiscent fruit with seed enclosed in a stony endocarp.

Eciliate ------------ without a marginal fringe of hairs.

Elliptic ------------ widest in center and the two ends equal.

Endemic ------------ restricted geographically to a single area.

Endocarp ---------- inner layer of pericarp.

Entire ------------- without toothing, lobing or division.

Evergreen ---------- bearing green leaves throughout the year.

Excurrent ---------- running out, as a nerve of a leaf projecting beyond the margin, or a midrib beyond the tip of the leaf.

Florets ------------- special term for a grass flower with its lemma and palea included (fig. 10).

Falcate --------------- curved sideways and flat, tapering up-
wards, sickle-shaped.

Funnelform --------- with the tube gradually widening upward and passing into the limb.

Glandular ----------- containing or bearing secreting organs
or glands.

Glaucous ------------ covered with a whitish substance that
rubs off or polishes to a gloss.

Glomerule----------- a dense crowded cluster, usually of
flowers.

Glume--------------- used for the 2 lower empty bracts of a
grass spikelet (fig. 12).

Habitat --------------- the kind of locality in which a plant
grows.

Head------------------ a dense cluster of sessile flowers or
fruit on a very short axis (fig. 15).

Imbricated ---------- overlapping, as shingles on a roof.

Indehiscent --------- remaining persistently closed, not opening along definite lines.

Inflorescence ------- type of arrangement of the flowering
part of a plant.

Involucre ------------ a set of bracts surrounding a flower
cluster, head or a simple flower (fig. 3).

Keel------------------- two lower united petals (fig. 21).

Lanceolate ---------- several times longer than wide,
broadest toward the base and tapering
to apex.

Lateral --------------- arising on the sides of an object.

Leaflet---------------- a single segment of a compound leaf
(fig. 7).

Legume -------------- fruit of *Leguminosae*; a pod.

Lemma--------------- the lower of the two bracts immediately
enclosing the flower in the grasses
(fig. 10).

Ligule---------------- a hair-like or membranous projection

	up from the inside of a grass sheath at its junction with the blade (fig. 11).
Linear	narrow and flat with sides parallel like a blade of grass.
Lobe	any segment of an organ especially if rounded (fig. 9).
Midrib	the central or main rib of a leaf (fig. 9).
Nerve	a simple or unbranched vein.
Node	point on stem from which leaves or branches arise.
Oblanceolate	lanceolate with the broadest portion towards the apex.
Oblong	two to four times longer than wide and the sides parallel or nearly so.
Obtuse	blunt or rounded at the apex.
Opposite	two leaves at a node; are situated across the stem from each other (fig. 4).
Orbicular	circular.
Oval	width more than one-half the length, egg-shaped.
Ovate	outline like an egg with the broader end at the base.
Ovoid	a solid with an egg-shaped outline.
Palea	the inner of the two bracts enclosing the gras flower (fig. 10).
Palmate	lobed or divided in a handlike fashion (fig. 22).
Panicle	a compound inflorescence with the younger flowers at the center (fig. 16).
Pedicel	the stem of an individual flower (fig. 2).
Peduncle	stem of a flower-cluster or of a solitary flower when that flower is the only member of the inflorescence (fig. 3).
Perennial	living several years.

228

Perianth------------- corolla and calyx considered together (fig. 1).

Pericarp------------- the wall of the matured ovary.

Petal---------------- one of the individual parts of the corolla (fig. 1).

Pinnate------------- compound leaf with the leaflets on two opposite sides of an elongated axis (fig. 23).

Pith ----------------- the soft spongy center of the stem of most plants.

Prostrate------------ flat on the ground.

Pubescent----------- covered with hairs.

Raceme------------- an inflorescence with pedicelled flowers borne along an elongated axis with the younger flowers nearest the top (fig. 17).

Racemose----------- in racemes.

Ray------------------ the strap-shaped flower in the *Compositae* used especially for marginal flowers different from the central regular ones (fig. 15).

Reflexed------------ bent backward.

Relic---------------- localized plants apparently surviving from past geological epochs.

Reniform------------ kidney-shaped.

Reticulate----------- having a network of leaf veins.

Rhizomatous-------- having a network of underground stems.

Rhizome------------- a prostrate, elongated stem growing underneath the suface of the ground.

Rosette-------------- a dense basal cluster of leaves arranged in a circular fashion.

Runner-------------- a long, slender, prostrate branch taking root at the nodes or tip.

Scabrous------------ rough to the touch.

Scales---------------- any thin, scarious body resembling the scales of a fish.

Scape---------------- a naked flowering stem arising from the ground without proper leaves.

Scarious-------------- thin, dry, membranous, and more or less translucent, not green.

Sepal---------------- one of the parts of the outer whorl of the calyx, usually green in color (fig. 1).

Serrate-------------- having sharp teeth directed forward.

Sessile-------------- without a stalk.

Sheath-------------- usually used for that part of the leaf of a sedge or grass that envelopes the stem (fig. 12).

Shrub-------------- a woody perennial, smaller than a tree, that usually has several stems or trunks from the base.

Simple-------------- of only one part, not completely divided into separate segments (fig. 8).

Sinus---------------- the space between two lobes (fig. 9).

Spadix-------------- a kind of spike or head with a thick or fleshy axis (fig. 20).

Spathe-------------- a large bract subtending and often enclosing an inflorescence (fig. 20).

Spike-------------- an inflorescence with the flowers sessile on a more or less elongated axis (fig. 18).

Spray-------------- the small branches or branchlets of trees, with their foliage.

Spur---------------- a hollow, sac-like or tubular extension of a floral organ.

Stamen-------------- one of the pollen bearing organs of a flower (fig. 1).

Stipule-------------- a pair of small structures at the base of the stalk of certain leaves (fig. 9).

230

Style ---------------- the stalk-like part of a pistil connecting the ovary and stigma (fig. 1).

Subglobose ---------- slightly round, like a model of the earth.

Subsessile ------------ somewhat sessile.

Subtended ----------- to be situated below and close to.

Sucker --------------- a vegetative shoot that originates underground.

Tendrils ------------- a slender outgrowth, serving as an organ of support and commonly coiling at the end.

Terminal ------------- at the tip end.

Tomentose ---------- covered with dense wool-like hairs.

Truncate ------------- squared at the tip or base as if cut off with a straight blade.

Tree ------------------ a woody plant that produces one main trunk.

Tuberous ------------ like a thickening into a short underground branch with numerous buds or eyes.

Tufts ----------------- stems in a very close cluster.

Umbel --------------- a flat-topped inflorescence, the flowers all arising from one point (fig. 19).

Undulate ------------- gently wavy, as a leaf margin.

Vine ------------------ a plant climbing on some support whose stem does not stand upright by itself.

Whorl --------------- a circle of three or more leaves, branches, or leaf-stalks arising from one node (fig. 6).

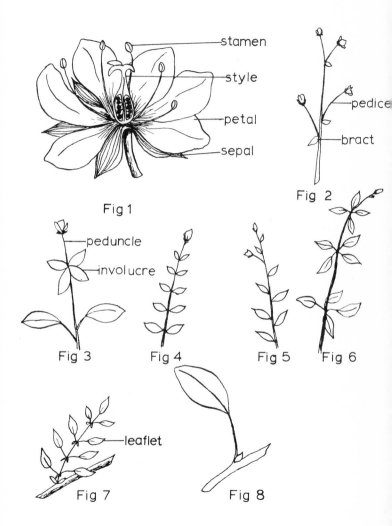

stamen

style

petal

sepal

Fig 1

pedicel

bract

Fig 2

peduncle

involucre

Fig 3

Fig 4

Fig 5

Fig 6

leaflet

Fig 7

Fig 8

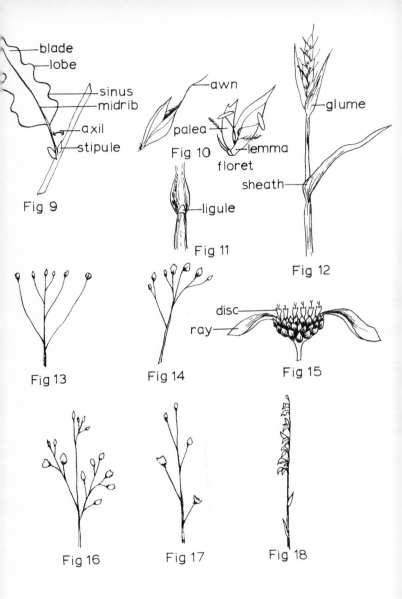

blade
lobe
sinus
midrib
axil
stipule

Fig 9

awn
palea
Fig 10
lemma
floret

ligule

Fig 11

glume

sheath

Fig 12

Fig 13

Fig 14

disc
ray

Fig 15

Fig 16

Fig 17

Fig 18

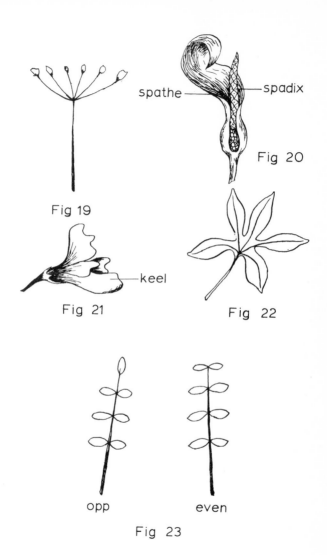

Fig 19

spathe — spadix

Fig 20

keel

Fig 21

Fig 22

opp   even

Fig 23

234

REFERENCES

Britton, Nathaniel Lord, and Addison Brown.
    1913. An illustrated flora of the northern United States, Canada, and the British possessions. Vols. I-III, 2052 p. Charles Scribner's Sons, NY.

Fernald, Merritt Lyndon.
    1950. Gray's manual of botany. 1632 p. American Book Co., NY.

Gleason, Henry A., and Arthur Conquist.
    1963. Manual of vascular plants of northeastern United States and adjacent Canada. 810 p. D. Van Nostrand Co., NY.

Harrington, H. D.
    1957. How to identify plants. 203 p. Sage Books, Denver, CO.

Kucera, Clair L.
    1961. The grasses of Missouri. 341 p. Univ. Missouri Press, Columbia, MO.

Missouri Department of Conservation and USDA Soil Conservation Service.
    1978. Rare and endangered species of Missouri. 76 p. MO Dept. of Conservation and USDA Soil Conservation Service, MO.

Palmer, Ernest J., and Julian A. Steyermark.
    1935. An annotated catalogue of the flowering plants of Missouri. Annals of the Missouri Botanical Garden 22:375-758.

Steyermark, Julian A.
    1963.   Flora of Missouri. 1725 p. The Iowa State University Press, Ames, IA.

United States Army Engineer District.
    1976.   An inventory of rare and endangered plant species found in the St. Louis, Missouri Corps of Engineers district. 281 p. U.S. Army Engineer District, St. Louis, MO.

United States Department of the Interior—Fish and Wildlife Service.
    1976.   Endangered and threatened species—plants. Federal Register Vol. 47, No. 117, p. 24524-24572.

RARE PLANT OBSERVATION DATA

1. Identification:

Family:
Scientific name:
Common name:

2. Location (be as specific as possible):

Section _____ Township _____ Range _____
Ownership _____

3. Type of Habitat:

Woods	_____	Glade	_____
Prairie	_____	Bottomland	_____
Bluff	_____	Sinkhole	_____
Bog	_____	Field	_____
Spring	_____	Streambank	_____
Roadside	_____	Other	_____

4. Stage of Growth:

Stage (dormant, bud, flower, seed):
Date:

5. Probable Status:

_____ Endangered
_____ Threatened
_____ Rare
_____ Unknown

6. Population Number (please check):

1-10	_____	50-100	_____
10-25	_____	100 or more	_____
25-50	_____		

7. **Existing Land Use (please check):**

Grazed	_____	Logged	_____
Ungrazed	_____	Sprayed	_____
Evidence of		Other	_____
recent fire	_____		

8. **Reported by:**

Name:
Address:
Affiliation (if any):

9. **Remarks:**